ER
KC

MW00667433

PRACTICAL PACKET RADIO

PACKET FREQ:- 145.01

STAN HORZEPA, WA1LOU

Published by: **The American Radio Relay League**
225 Main Street
Newington, CT 06111-1494

Printed in USA

First Edition
Second Printing, 1998

This book is dedicated to my dear Mother.
If not for her, this book would not be and neither would me.

Stan Horzepa, WA1LOU

Contents

Foreword

We live in a digital world. Our telephone conversations, TV pictures and even the world of commercial information—via the Internet—are digital or have digital components. As with all communications breakthroughs, radio amateurs have been at the forefront of the digital revolution. By far the most popular digital mode, packet radio has been evolving—and becoming ever more popular—since the early 1980s. In 1987 the ARRL published the first authoritative packet radio book, *Your Gateway to Packet Radio*, by Stan Horzepa, WA1LOU. *Your Gateway* remained popular through two editions and five printings.

Not content to have created and developed the most popular new mode since FM, inventive hams have made possible a host of new ways to use packet radio to communicate and exchange information. Connection to the Internet, wormholes and APRS are but a few examples.

Packet radio appeals to both experienced hams and newcomers, technology wizards and communicators. When it came time to replace *Your Gateway to Packet Radio*, we asked an experienced author—none other than Stan, WA1LOU—to write the new book. His assignment: Write clearly enough to guide a newcomer, but comprehensively enough to make the book a complete and authoritative source for all packet-active hams. This up-to-date book is the result.

We hope you'll tell us how you like it. Drop a note to Editor, *Practical Packet Radio*, or use the handy Feedback Form near the back.

David Sumner, K1ZZ
Executive Vice President
November 1995

Introduction

Section 1

Packet radio—where did it start. A brief introduction before we begin.

1

Introduction

August 19, 1985 was a historic day. At 9 AM that day, Tucson Amateur Packet Radio (TAPR) opened the phone lines and began taking orders for a brand new packet radio controller, the TAPR TNC 2. There were only 280 TNC 2 kits available for immediate shipment, so placing an order for one was like trying to win a lottery.

After several unsuccessful attempts trying to get through to TAPR, I finally made a connection in the early afternoon and was greeted by Packet Pete Eaton, WB9FLW, who informed me that I was lucky caller number MXYZPTLK. I don't remember which number caller I was, but I do remember my order was one of the original batch of 280 kits and I was ecstatic.

Those were exciting times! All the local packet operators were in a frenzy about the new TNC. At that time, we were using a variety of equipment (Vancouver boards, TAPR TNC 1s, GLB PK1s, etc.), some of it barely adequate and we were anxious to upgrade to something better. TAPR TNC 2 was something better, something much better and the hobby recognized it as such.

So many calls came into TAPR that day that they overloaded and shut down the Tucson telephone center several times. After 832 orders, TAPR turned off the phones. Soon after, AEA, Kantronics, MFJ, PacComm and others licensed the TNC 2 from TAPR and began producing them by the truckloads. And they sold by the truckloads, too!

The TNC 2 had a revolutionary effect on amateur packet radio. Before the TNC 2, there were perhaps one, maybe two thousand TNCs in operation worldwide. A decade later, multiply those numbers a hundred times and you have a conservative estimate of what is out there today.

Along with the TNC explosion came an explosion of TNC users who wanted to do something with this new technology besides ragchew (not that there is anything wrong with ragchewing). They wanted to apply packet radio to perform new tasks. They wanted to do something practical with packet radio. And, that is what this book is all about, practical packet radio.

Installation

Section 2

Before you can use packet radio for practical applications, you must put a packet radio station together. This section describes what pieces you need to complete the packet radio puzzle. It also explains how to fit the pieces together and how to make sure all the pieces work together correctly.

2

Requirements

You can divide an amateur packet radio installation into three parts: packet radio equipment, terminal equipment, and radio equipment.

This chapter describes these three basic components and how they are interconnected.

PACKET RADIO EQUIPMENT

A *packet assembler-disassembler* (*PAD*) is a circuit that assembles and disassembles packets. The PAD accepts data from a terminal and formats it into packet frames for transmission via a communications medium. The PAD also accepts packet frames received via a communications medium, extracts data from the packet frames and transfers the data to a terminal.

In amateur packet radio, a PAD is connected to a *modem* to convert (*modulate*) the digital signals from the PAD into analog signals for transmission by an Amateur Radio transmitter and to accept analog signals from an Amateur Radio receiver and translate (*demodulate*) them into digital signals for transfer to the PAD. (Modem is a contraction of modulator-demodulator.)

Terminal Node Controller (TNC)

In the beginning, a *terminal node controller* (*TNC*) was a PAD designed specifically for amateur packet radio operations. Today, a TNC includes both the PAD and

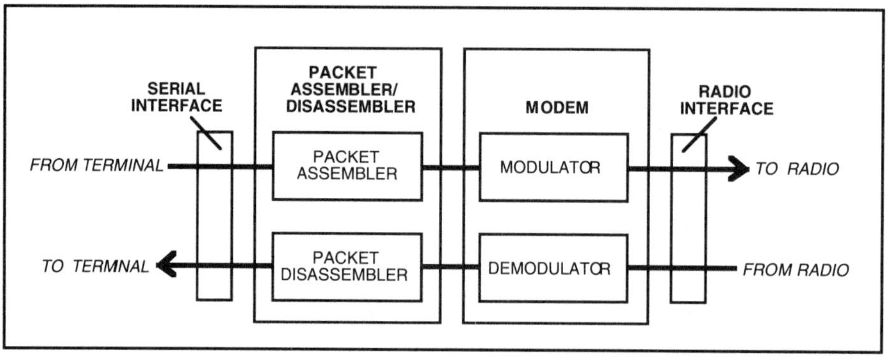

Fig 2-1—The functional block diagram of a typical TNC.

modem functions, thus eliminating the requirement of adding an external modem to a PAD-only TNC. (Fig 2-1 is the functional block diagram of a typical TNC.)

In addition to a modem, the primary components in a typical amateur packet radio TNC are a microprocessor, an HDLC controller, interfaces and memory.

The microprocessor supervises the other components according to the packet radio *protocol* software stored in the *read-only memory* (*ROM*) of the TNC. *AX.25 Amateur Packet-Radio Link-Layer Protocol, Version 2.0* (*AX.25* for short) is the packet radio protocol used by most TNCs today. For a description of how AX.25 works, refer to Appendix A.

The HDLC controller formats data from the microprocessor into the frames that are transmitted over the air and it extracts data from each received frame for transfer to the microprocessor. In addition, the HDLC calculates the *frame check sequence* (*FCS*) when a frame is assembled in preparation for transmission and recalculates the FCS for each frame received over the air to check its integrity.

The interface provides for the transfer of data and commands between the TNC and the terminal. Typically, this interface is a *serial interface* that is compatible with EIA-232 specifications. Another interface, the radio interface, provides for the transfer of the analog packet signals between the radio equipment and the modem in the TNC. This interface also turns the radio transmitter on and off.

Various forms of memory are also included in a TNC. The TNC uses ROM (read-only memory), typically in the form of an *erasable programmable ROM* (*EPROM*), to permanently store the packet radio *protocol* software. The TNC uses *random access memory* (*RAM*) to store information temporarily (frames in queue for transmission, received frames and system variables). Also, the TNC uses *Nonvolatile RAM* (*NVRAM*, *NV-RAM* or *NOVRAM*) or *battery-backed RAM* (*bbRAM*) to store TNC parameters that may be changed by the user. Such RAM will store data even after the TNC is turned off.

TNC Types

TNCs come in a variety of flavors. What follows is a summary of the major types of packet radio equipment:

- PADs, also known as TNCs, that require external modems; a PAD never includes a built-in modem, but a TNC may or may not include a built-in modem

- TNCs with modems that are designed for VHF applications (1200-baud, Bell 202 compatible)
- TNCs with modems that may be selected for 1200-baud VHF and 300-baud HF applications; most TNCs today are of this type
- TNCs with separate modems for VHF and HF applications; separate VHF and HF radio ports permit the simultaneous connection of VHF and HF radio equipment
- TNCs with modems that operate at data rates other than 300 and 1200 bauds.
- TNCs designed to be used only with specific computers, for example, TNCs on a card you install in a PC expansion port
- TNCs that operate in other Amateur Radio modes; these are known as *multimode controllers*
- *TNC emulators*, that is, computer software that performs all the functions of a TNC except the modem function

PAD-only TNCs that require external modems are seldom seen today, but you may encounter them in the used equipment market. The primary source of this TNC type was *Vancouver Amateur Digital Communications Group* (*VADCG*, the Canadian ham radio club that got amateur packet radio rolling) and Bill Ashby & Son.

TNCs with various modem configurations (VHF-only, VHF or HF, VHF and HF, high speed) have been produced by the "Big Four" TNC manufacturers (AEA, Kantronics, MFJ and PacComm) for over a decade and the Big Four continues to produce them today. GLB, Heath and TAPR were past producers of these TNCs that you may encounter in the used equipment market.

Fig 2-2—These 1990s style TNCs are capable of 1200 and 9600 bit/s operation: the AEA PK-96, Kantronics KPC-9612, MFJ-1270C and PacComm TNC/NB96.

Today, PacComm and Hamilton and Area Packet Network (HAPN) are the main providers of computer-specific TNCs, that is, TNCs on a PC expansion card. In the past, DRSI also produced such a card and AEA produced a TNC that plugged into a Commodore C64 computer.

Multimode controllers are devices that do packet radio as well as one or more other Amateur Radio modes such as CW, Baudot RTTY, ASCII RTTY, AMTOR, PacTOR, FAX, Navtex, SSTV, etc. If you wish to operate a variety of modes, you should consider purchasing a multimode controller (the Big Four all produce them). However, if you wish only to operate packet radio, then buy a TNC. A TNC is less expensive, takes up less space, and consumes less power than a multimode controller. A TNC is the economical choice for the packet-only operator.

TNC emulation software is available for Apple Macintosh, Commodore C64/128, and IBM-PC/MS-DOS-class computers. In all cases, you connect a VHF packet modem to your computer and run the software that emulates the functions of a TNC. Sigma Design Associates produces the Macintosh TNC emulation system, MFJ offers the Commodore system, and PacComm and Tigertronics produce PC versions. In the past, modems (kits and assembled) and shareware software have been available from a variety of sources and may still show up sporadically.

Modems

When the amateur packet radio pioneers looked for a modem to connect to their first TNCs, Bell 202 modems were readily available as surplus equipment. As a result, Bell 202 modems were used in early packet radio applications and continue to be used today, primarily in VHF 1200-baud applications. Most TNCs that have internal modems for 1200-bit/s applications are compatible with Bell 202.

"Bell" refers to modems that are compatible with the standards that were developed by the United States telephone company, American Telephone and Telegraph Co. (AT&T). Different Bell standards were developed for different applications and each standard is designated by a three digit number and an optional letter. Bell 103 and Bell 212A are two examples. (Note that Bell modems are not compatible with the modem standards or "recommendations" that were developed by the *International Telegraph and Telephone Consultative Committee* (*CCITT*). CCITT recommendations are designated with the letter V, followed by a period and a two digit number; for example, CCITT Recommendation V.21.)

Bell 202 modems are *asynchronous*, *half-duplex* devices that operate at a maximum of 1200 bit/s using *frequency-shift keying* (*FSK*) with a *mark* frequency of 1200 Hz and a *space* frequency of 2200 Hz.

In FSK, the transmitted carrier is modulated between two frequencies (the mark and space frequencies). In HDLC of a TNC, the mark and space designations do not directly relate to the state (0 or 1) of a data bit. Rather, a 0 bit is indicated by a change between mark and space (or space and mark), while a 1 bit causes no change in the transmitted frequency. The encoding system is called *non-return to zero, inverted* (*NRZI*) encoding, and it is an integral part of the AX.25 specification.

Half-duplex is the ability to transmit and receive at different times, that is, not simultaneously or *full-duplex*. A Bell 202 modem cannot transmit and receive simultaneously on one channel.

Asynchronous refers to the fact that there is no direct relationship between the timing of the modulated signals of the modem and the timing of the transmitted data. The beginning and end of each received bit must be determined by the digital device connected to the modem. (*Synchronous* is another form of data transmission which uses the internal clock in the modem to synchronize data.)

Bell 103 modems are often used in HF 300-baud applications. Bell 103s are asynchronous, full-duplex modems that operate at a maximum of 300 bit/s using FSK. Full-duplex telephone line operation is achieved by using different mark and space frequency pairs at each end of the data communications circuit. At one end, the modem transmits on frequency pair F1 and receives on frequency pair F2, while at the other end, the modem transmits on frequency pair F2 and receives on frequency pair F1. (F1 marks are 1270 Hz, F1 spaces are 1070 Hz; F2 marks are 2225 Hz, F2 spaces are 2025 Hz.) HF packet radio applications are half-duplex and do not take advantage of the Bell 103 full-duplex capability even though the narrow 200-Hz shift between mark and space (as compared with the Bell 202 1000-Hz shift) provides a smaller signal bandwidth for HF transmissions.

The majority of packet radio modems used today are either Bell 202s or Bell 103s. However, some packet radio operations use other types of modems to achieve better performance.

High Speed

Modems that operate above 1200 bit/s are available today for the purpose of increasing packet radio *throughput*, that is, the amount of data that is transferred successfully during a specific amount of time. For example, 4800 bit/s has a better throughput than 1200 bit/s theoretically. In this example, 4800 and 1200 bits are the amount of data transferred successfully and 1 second is the specific amount of time used to measure the transfer.

The first step beyond 1200 bit/s is 2400 bit/s. Currently, only MFJ offers a 2400 bit/s modem as an option in their TNCs. In the past, Kantronics' KPC-2400 TNC included a 2400 bit/s *phase-shift keying* (*PSK*) modem. The next step is 4800 bit/s. HAPN is currently the only provider of modems at this speed.

Most of the high speed action is at 9600 bit/s. Years ago, Steve Goode, K9NG, designed a 9600 bit/s FSK modem. However, James Miller, G3RUH, improved upon K9NG's design and, today, the G3RUH design is the modem of choice at 9600 bit/s. Today, the Big Four and TAPR all offer G3RUH 9600 bit/s modems, either including a TNC or as an external modem. DRSI was a G3RUH modem provider in the past.

Nineteen dot two (19.2k/19,200 bit/s) is the domain of Kantronics. Their 19,200 bit/s Data Engine TNC is a big step up from 9600 bit/s, but the highest packet radio data rate (so far) has been achieved by Dale Heatherington, WA4DSY, and the Georgia Radio Amateur Packet Enthusiast Society (GRAPES). The GRAPES modem operates at the nose-bleed speed of 56,000 bit/s using bandwidth-limited *medium shift keying* (*MSK*).

Currently, AEA and TAPR offer *digital signal processing* (*DSP*) units that are capable of providing almost every imaginable packet radio modem you could ask for. And it is all accomplished by means of software within the unit! Needless to say, this equipment is expensive, but it is a lot less expensive than buying each individual modem that the DSP units support. So, if you need a lot of different modems, a DSP-based unit is the way to go. (Note that AEA's DSPs are assembled, whereas TAPR's is a kit.)

TERMINAL EQUIPMENT: THE USER INTERFACE

The *terminal* equipment provides the direct interface to the user. Via the terminal keyboard, the user enters commands that control the TNC and, when communications are established, the user enters information on that same keyboard for transmission to the other station in the communications link. The terminal display allows the user to read the TNC's responses to the user's commands and to read the information that is being sent by the other station.

In general, the terminal equipment you will find in an amateur packet radio station falls into one of two categories: dedicated terminals and computers that are emulating terminals.

Dedicated Terminal Equipment

A dedicated terminal (*terminal* or *DTE*, for short) is a device that is designed for the single purpose of communicating with computers. Terminals are available in a wide variety. Today, the most common terminal consists of some kind of video display, a keyboard and a serial interface (typically EIA-232 compatible). This type of terminal is sometimes called a *video-display terminal* (*VDT*). The VDT may be a simple device that provides basic input and output functions (commonly called a *dumb terminal*), or it may provide numerous support functions as well as basic input and output (this device is commonly known as an *intelligent terminal*).

Some older terminals may use a printer instead of a video display for output, or they may use a paper-tape reader instead of a keyboard for input. Instead of an EIA-232 serial port, older terminals may use dc "loop" current for interfacing to external equipment. By their nature, the data rate of such devices is slow. High-speed line printers are still used today for hard-copy data output, but paper-tape reading equipment is considered obsolete.

Computers Emulating Terminals

In the typical packet station, a computer emulates a DTE by running *terminal emulation software*. Such software comes in a variety of flavors. The two most popular flavors in packet radio are software intended for data communications over the telephone line with a modem and software designed specifically for packet radio terminal emulation.

If you have software for use with a telephone line modem, it is very likely that it can be used for packet radio, too. After all, a TNC is essentially an intelligent modem that communicates over the airwaves rather than the telephone lines. Such software will serve you well in the packet radio mode and, if you already have it, it is one less item that you have to get to set up your packet station.

For packet radio applications, communication software should, at a minimum, have a few simple commands for clearing the screen, moving the cursor, backspacing and tabbing. Also, such software should be capable of operating at a data rate that is compatible with the serial port of your packet radio equipment. In addition, the software should be capable of saving received data in memory and/or in storage (on disk). The software should also be capable of sending data that has been previously stored. Simultaneous hard-copy printing of what the terminal receives and sends is also a good feature.

The drawback with most telephone line communication software is that it is designed to operate primarily with telephone-line modems, not packet radio modems (TNCs). As a result, these programs include features that are only useful for telephone data communications and are useless to the packet radio operator. Most of these programs also lack features that the packet radio operator would find useful.

Software specifically designed for packet radio terminal emulation offers more features to facilitate packet radio communications than a telephone line terminal emulator offers. For example, if you communicate with more than one station simulta-

Packet Radio Terminal Emulation Software

Packet radio terminal emulators are available as commercial packages (you pay for it before you use it), shareware (you use it before you pay for it and only if you like it), and freeware (you use it for free). A sampling of this software for our more popular computers follows (refer to Appendix E for the address and phone numbers of the commercial suppliers listed below).

Apple II

APR—An Apple II/II+/IIe/IIc/IIgs packet program that is available by sending a blank 5.25- or 3.5-inch disk and a postage-paid, self-addressed disk mailer to Larry East, W1HUE, 1355 Rimline Dr., Idaho Falls, ID 83401.

Apple Macintosh

Host Master Mac—Kantronics' packet terminal program for the Mac that is optimized for the Kantronics' TNC line.

MacRATT with FAX—A full-featured packet terminal program from AEA that is optimized for AEA's TNCs, but runs well with other TNC brands, too.

Savant—Sigma Design Associates' Macintosh DTE and TNC emulator that does *not* require a TNC to do packet. All you need is an external modem, the PacketMac, and *SoftKiss*, the modem software driver. *Savant* will also run with any TNC in the KISS mode.

Atari

Packet—A packet terminal emulator for Atari 8-bit computers from Electrosoft.

IBM-PC

Host Master II+—Kantronics' packet terminal program for the PC that is optimized for the Kantronics' TNC line.

PaKet—A full-featured packet terminal program that runs under DOS, OS/2, and UNIX-DOS/Merge. It is available from Jim Flannery, WBØNZW, 8098 S Carr Ct., Littleton, CO 80123.

PC-PAKRATT for DOS—A full-featured packet terminal program from AEA that is optimized for AEA's TNCs.

PHSOS2.ZIP—An OS/2 multimode terminal emulator for the AEA PK-232 and PK-900 controllers may be downloaded from CompuServe's HamNet.

XPCOM—A Windows multimode terminal emulator for the AEA PK-232 and MFJ-1278 multimode controllers may be downloaded from CompuServe's HamNet.

neously (a multiconnect situation), some packet radio terminal emulators allow you to open separate communications windows for each station you are connected to. No telephone line software offers that feature. If you become dissatisfied using telephone line software in the packet radio mode, you might consider getting a program specifically designed for packet radio. The accompanying sidebar, "Packet-Radio Terminal Emulation Software," lists what is available.

Terminals Vs. Computers

Using a dedicated terminal or using a computer emulating a terminal both have advantages and disadvantages for packet radio applications. Expense is always a consideration. On one hand, a good, used terminal may be less expensive than a new, but barely adequate computer. On the other hand, a good used computer may be less expensive than a new but barely adequate terminal.

The function of a terminal is to communicate. If you dedicate a terminal to packet radio communications, it is doing the job it was intended to do. A computer can serve a variety of functions, however, and dedicating it to packet radio applications may underutilize its abilities and be a waste of hardware and money.

Terminals are designed specifically for communications, while computers are not. This means that computers are not necessarily good communication tools. How good a communications tool a computer is depends on its communications software. One great advantage computers have over terminals is their ability to store data in memory and/or in a storage medium (on disk). Most terminals have no means of storing data.

All of these considerations must be weighed when you decide what to use to communicate with your packet radio equipment.

Whatever you use as a DTE, it must be capable of interfacing with your TNC. Almost all TNCs use the EIA-232 interface with its ubiquitous 25-pin connector to provide a serial connection to a DTE, so your DTE should have an EIA-232 interface as well.

Most real DTEs have an EIA-232 interface, so connecting them to a TNC is simple. On the other hand, computers don't necessarily have EIA-232 interfaces. Some computers have no interface. EIA-232 may be an option that requires adding a printed circuit board to the computer. (If you have an IBM-PC/MS-DOS class computer, add a TNC-on-an-expansion-card to your PC instead of the EIA-232 interface and avoid the serial interface middleman altogether.)

Some computers use other interfaces. For example, EIA-422 is found on a few computers, including the Macintosh. EIA-422 is close enough to EIA-232 that it can be made to work with it by properly wiring interfaces together.

Getting back to EIA-232. . . although it supports 25 signals, most TNCs only need three of them (the signals on pins 2, 3 and 7), so check your TNC manual and see what you can do to economize your DTE-to-TNC cabling. (If you own a telephone line modem, it's a good bet that the cable you use with it will work with your TNC, too.)

RF EQUIPMENT: THE RADIO CONNECTION

The radio equipment transmits and receives packets. It includes a transceiver (or separate transmitter and receiver), an antenna and any peripheral radio equipment (amplifier, preamplifier, tuner, feed line and so on). Some of this equipment is of little concern to us. For example, as long as the antennas and feed line are capable of putting a signal on the desired packet radio frequency, that satisfies our requirements. Other RF hardware needs closer inspection, however.

Our primary concern is the radio equipment's receive-to-transmit and transmit-to-receive *turnaround times*. This is the amount of time it takes for a transmitter to be ready to transmit and a receiver to be ready to receive after a switch between the transmit and receive modes occurs. A TNC can switch between the transmit and receive modes very quickly, so quickly that it usually must wait for the RF equipment before it can continue to communicate. Most amateur radios have receive-to-transmit and transmit-to-receive turnaround times between 150 and 400 milliseconds (ms), which dramatically reduces the amount of data that can be sent and increases the chance that two or more stations will interfere with one another. Such delays slow down what is intended to be a fast mode of communication.

The actual physical switching of an antenna, internally in a transceiver or externally with a separate transmitter and receiver, is one factor that affects the turnaround time. The older the transceiver, the more likely that the switching is performed mechanically by some kind of relay. If a separate transmitter and receiver are used with one antenna, there is also likely to be a mechanical relay performing the switch. In addition, if an external power amplifier and/or receive preamplifier is used, more mechanical switching is likely to be involved.

With newer equipment, the switching is more likely to be accomplished electronically. This speeds up the process, but this improvement may be compromised by the frequency synthesizer circuitry used by newer RF equipment. After switching between the transmit and receive modes, all synthesizers require some time to lock on frequency before they are ready to transmit or receive. Older RF equipment does not use frequency synthesis and does not have this delay. Some new equipment is being designed with packet radio in mind, and synthesizers that can lock more quickly are now being offered. If you are out hunting for a new transceiver for packet radio applications, keep this feature in mind.

Another problem is that the modem-to-radio interface of most of the radios used for packet radio depends on audio response filters and audio levels intended for microphones and speakers, which, more often than not, leads to incorrect deviation of the transmitted signal, noise and hum on the audio, and so on. Splatter filters and deviation limiters distort frequency response and further reduce the performance of the packet radio system. You are stuck in this environment unless you want to modify the radio. The problem is, trying to perform surgery on your typical VHF/UHF FM voice transceiver is difficult to impossible because of the use of LSIs, surface mounting and miniaturization.

Instead of using an average amateur transceiver for packet radio (and avoiding some of the compromises that involves), there are alternatives that solve many of the RF equipment problems that have been discussed. The solution comes in the guise of high-speed RF equipment that is optimized for packet radio operation. Today, Alinco, Kantronics, MFJ, Tekk and others offer such packet radio radios.

1995

3

Interconnection

The actual physical installation of a packet radio station is straightforward. Basically, you connect your TNC to your terminal and your RF equipment.

TNC-TO-TERMINAL CONNECTION

Most TNCs are designed to be connected to a terminal by means of a serial port that is compatible with EIA standards EIA-232. In most cases, the omnipresent 25-pin subminiature D-type connector provides the actual physical connection to the TNC. If your terminal or computer also has an EIA-compatible interface, the connection is accomplished by means of a 25-wire cable with the appropriate connectors at each end. Appropriate, in this case, refers to connector gender. According to industry standards, a DTE has a male connector on its serial port while a DCE has a female connector. The DTE in this case is your terminal or computer and the DCE is your TNC. This means that the appropriate cable would have a 25-pin male connector at the TNC end and a 25-pin female connector at the terminal/computer end. This standard is not always adhered to, however.

Cables containing 25 wires are expensive. As the sidebar EIA-232 Signal Connections indicates, all 25 pins of the interface are not used by your TNC. Interconnections between pins 2, 3 and 7 will be adequate for almost all applications. A 3-wire cable is certainly less expensive than a 25-wire cable. Even less expensive is not needing a cable at all! If you already have a cable connecting your terminal or computer to a telephone line modem, it is very likely that you can use that same cable to connect your computer to your TNC. Fig 3-1 illustrates the TNC-to-terminal interconnection.

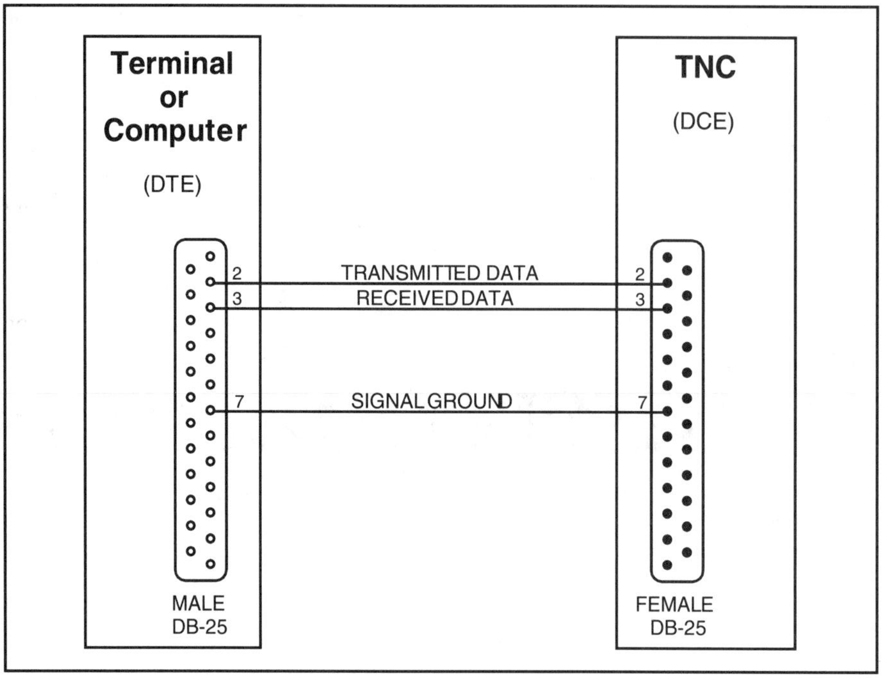

Fig 3-1—The minimal TNC-to-terminal interconnection.

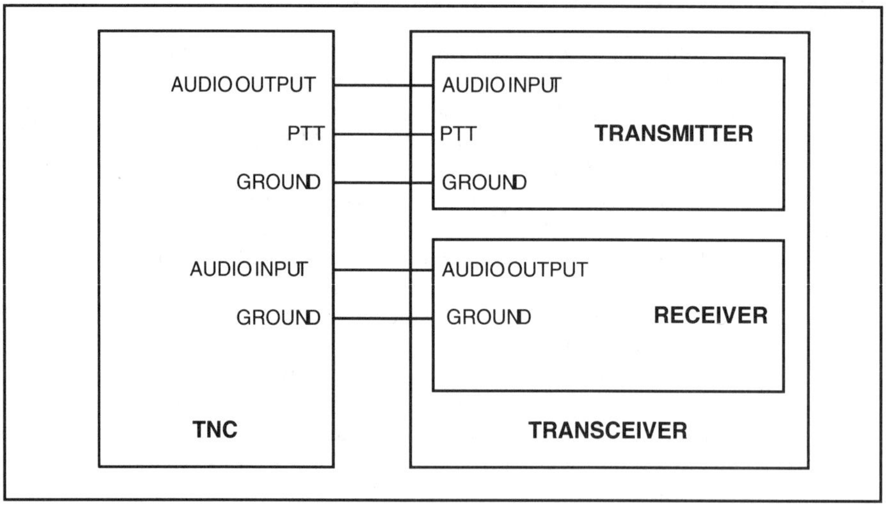

Fig 3-2—A typical TNC-to-radio interconnection.

If your terminal or computer does not have an EIA interface, you will have to add one. EIA interfaces are available as optional equipment or from third-party sources for some computers.

TNC-TO-RADIO CONNECTION

In most cases, the connection of a TNC to RF equipment is a matter of making a few simple connections. Fig 3-2 illustrates the TNC-to-radio interconnection.

The audio output of the TNC is connected to the audio input of your transmitter/transceiver. Typically, the audio input of your radio equipment is a microphone connector, but some transceivers have separate audio inputs for AFSK tones. If such a connection is available, it's better to use that connection rather than the microphone input, because it means you will not have to disconnect the packet radio equipment when you want to use the radio in the voice mode. In addition, the transceiver may have circuitry that processes the AFSK input signals in some way, and such processing would probably be beneficial to your packet radio signal as well.

The push-to-talk (PTT) line from your TNC is connected to a PTT connection on your transmitter/transceiver. Usually, PTT is available at the radio's microphone connector, but the PTT line is sometimes brought out to another jack as well. Again, connection to the optional PTT jack is preferable; this avoids cable changes when you switch modes.

The audio output of your receiver/transceiver is connected to the audio input of your TNC. Typically, the audio output of your radio is a speaker or headphone connector, but some radios have optional audio outputs (sometimes labeled "AFSK out"). Again, connection to such an optional audio output avoids cable changes, and the receiver/transceiver may provide some filtering or processing of the AFSK output signals. If your radio does not have separate AFSK jacks, the phone patch input and output jacks often provide an acceptable alternative.

In addition to these three connections, there must be a ground connection between your TNC and the transceiver (or transmitter and receiver).

Some transmitters/transceivers, typically VHF and UHF handheld transceivers, use a common conductor for audio input and PTT. Simply connecting the TNC's audio output and PTT leads to the common conductor on the radio will not work. To make the connection successfully, a capacitor and resistor are often required in the wiring circuit. Consult the manual that accompanies your radio for what is required to complete this connection.

To prevent RFI, all cables should be shielded. If shielding does not prevent RFI, the cables from the TNC to the radio should be wound around a toroid. If RFI is still a problem, wind the cabling between the TNC and the terminal and all ac line cables around toroids, too. Check *Radio Frequency Interference*, published by the ARRL, for more information on the causes and cures of RFI.

While we are on the topic of interference, we should mention that there is a problem with the design of the original TAPR TNC 2 that causes the TNC's clock to place a *birdie* around 145.0 MHz. If the birdie is interfering with your packet radio reception, you can make it migrate by replacing C47 with a 60-pF trimmer capacitor (on early versions of the TNC 2; later versions already have the trimmer capacitor installed). Tune the capacitor slightly to pull the birdie off your favorite 2-meter packet radio

EIA-232 SIGNAL CONNECTIONS

Designation			
Pin No.	*EIA*	*CCITT*	*Signal Name*
1	-	-	Shield
2	BA	103	Transmitted Data
3	BB	104	Received Data
4	CA	105	Request to Send
5	CB	106	Clear to Send
6	CC	107	DCE Ready
7	AB	102	Signal Ground
8	CF	109	Received Line Signal Detector
9	-	-	Reserved for DCE testing
10	-	-	Reserved for DCE testing
11	-	-	Unassigned
12	SCF	122	Secondary Received Line Signal Detector
13	SCB	121	Secondary Clear to Send
14	SBA	118	Secondary Transmitted Data
15	DB	114	Transmitter Signal Element Timing (DCE Source)
16	SBB	119	Secondary Received Data
17	DD	115	Receiver Signal Element Timing
18	LL	141	Local Loopback
19	SCA	120	Secondary Request to Send
20	CD	108.2	DTE Ready
21	CG/RL	110/140	Signal Quality Detector/Remote Loopback
22	CE	125	Ring Detector
23	CH/CI	111/112	Data Signal Rate Selector (DTE/DCE Source)
24	DA	113	Transmitter Signal Element Timing (DTE Source)
25	TM	142	Test Mode

EIA-232 is a standard recommended by the EIA (Electronic Industries Association) for the interface between data terminal equipment (DTE) and data communication equipment (DCE) employing serial binary data interchange.

A description of the EIA RS-232-C/EIA-232-D signals that are of most concern in a packet radio installation follows:

• *Transmitted Data*, pin 2, is intelligence from the DTE that is intended for transmission by the DCE (TNC) over the communication medium (RF).

• *Received Data*, pin 3, is intelligence from the DCE (TNC) that was received over the communication medium (RF) and demodulated by the DCE (TNC).

• *Signal Ground*, pin 7, provides a common ground reference for all the other interface signals except Shield, pin 1.

channel. C47 is located next to the crystal, Y1, near the center of the TNC printed-circuit board.

EXTERNAL MODEMS

The original TAPR TNC 2 design included a *modem disconnect* connector on its circuit board. This connector permits you to easily connect an external modem, such as a high speed modem, to the TNC (and bypass the TNC internal modem).

Problem is that some manufacturers that cloned the TNC 2 did not include a modem disconnect connector in their clone design. As a result, adding an external modem to these TNCs is more difficult, if not impossible.

If your TNC does not have a modem disconnect connector, consult its manual or manufacturer for advice as to how to add an external modem. It may be easier to get a TNC that does have the connector than try to modify your TNC to accept an external modem.

4

Programming

You have connected your TNC to a terminal and transceiver and are anxious to let your first packet fly through the air. Before that happens, you have to make sure that your TNC is compatible with your terminal and transceiver.

Whether your terminal is compatible or not depends on the hardware and the software. There is not much you can do about the hardware (besides getting another terminal). If the terminal is actually a computer running terminal-emulation software, then the compatibility depends on the flexibility of that software. If the software is not adequate, you can try a different program. The transceiver is less flexible. If your transceiver is not suitable, you will probably have to get a different transceiver (unless you are adept at modifying LSI and microprocessor circuits).

Luckily, your TNC is very flexible. It may be adapted for use with almost any terminal and transceiver that can be connected to it. What follows is a checklist of parameters that you may set to make your TNC compatible with your terminal and transceiver.

DATA RATE

Data rate is the speed at which information is transferred. This speed may be measured as bits per second or *baud*. In most applications, a baud is equal to one digital bit of information per second. As a result, the terms data rate, *baud* and *bit rate* are used interchangeably (refer to the sidebar titled "Bauds Vs. Bits Per Second").

Your TNC communicates with your terminal by means of its *serial port* (usually a female 25-pin D-type connector) and with a transceiver by means of its radio port

OR "9" PIN

Bauds vs. Bits Per Second

There seems to be some confusion among radio amateurs as to the meaning of the terms *bauds* and *bits per second* as used to describe data-transmission rates. The two terms are *not* interchangeable.

Bauds are used to describe the *signaling rate* (or *symbol rate*). This is a measure of how fast individual signal elements *could be* transmitted through a communications system. Specifically, the baud is defined as the reciprocal of the shortest element (in seconds) in the data encoding scheme. For example, in a system where the shortest element is 1 ms long, the signaling rate would be 1000 elements per second. Instead of using elements per second, the term baud is used (incidentally, this is why it is not correct to refer to the "baud rate"; since baud already means elements per second, "baud rate" means "elements per second rate," something like "miles per hour speed"). Continuous transmission is not required, since signaling speed is based only on the shortest signal element.

Signaling rate in bauds says nothing about actual *information transfer rate*. The maximum information transfer rate is defined as the number of equivalent binary digits transferred per second; this is measured in *bits per second*.

So far, everything seems fairly simple. The complications arise when more sophisticated data encoding schemes are used. When binary data encoding is used, each signaling element represents one bit. In a quadriphase system, a phase transition of 90 degrees represents a level shift. There are four possible states in a QPSK system; since two binary bits are required to represent four possible levels, each state can represent two binary bits. If 1000 elements per second are transmitted in a quadriphase system where each element can represent two bits, the actual information rate is 2000 bit/s.

This scheme can be extended. It is possible to transmit three bits at a time using eight different phase angles (bit/s = 3 × bauds). In addition, each angle can have more than one amplitude. A standard 9600-bit/s modem uses 12 phase angles, four of which have two amplitude values. This yields 16 distinct states; each state can then represent four binary bits. Using this technique, the information transfer rate is four times the signaling speed. This is what makes it possible to transfer data over a phone line at a rate that would produce an unacceptable bandwidth using binary encoding. This also makes it possible to transfer data at 2400 bits/s on 10 meters, where FCC regulations allow only 1200-baud signals.

When are transmission speed in bauds and information rate in bit/s equal? Three conditions must be met: binary encoding must be used, all elements used to encode characters must be equal in width and synchronous transmission at a constant rate must be used. In all other cases, the two terms are not equivalent. Each term is important at a different location in a communications link. Information transfer rate is most important to the communicator; how the information gets where it is going makes no difference. The link designer, however, need only worry about the signaling rate; the number of bits per baud is unimportant at this level.—*Bruce Hale, KB1MW*

(usually a female 5-pin DIN connector). A serial port transfers digital information bit-by-bit (serially) as opposed to transferring information character-by-character or byte-by-byte (in parallel). The data rate of the radio port is independent of the serial port data rate. The rates are selected either by hardware or software. The radio-port data rate determines how fast you communicate with other packet-radio stations over the air. The terminal-port data rate determines how fast your TNC communicates with your terminal.

Serial Port Speed

The data rate of your TNC serial port and the data rate of the terminal connected to your TNC must be the same. If the terminal has selectable data rates, you should set the terminal (and your TNC serial port) to the highest data rate that allows successful communication between the terminal and your TNC. A data rate of 2400 or 4800 bit/s is acceptable. When you send a command to your TNC at those data rates, you will see the responses instantly, and messages received over the air will be printed almost the instant they are received by your TNC. (Higher data rates provide even quicker communication. Some TNCs do not operate reliably at those rates, however, so you will need to experiment to see if your TNC can handle it.)

The serial port of some TNCs may be set to data rates of 300, 1200, 2400, 4800 and 9600 bit/s by means of a rear panel DIP switch. Fig 4-1 shows how to position the TNC rear-panel DIP switch for each of these data rates. Make sure that the TNC is turned off when you select the serial-port data rate.

Some TNCs do not use a DIP switch to set the serial port data rate. Rather, they use *autobaud* to select the serial port data rate automatically. To use autobaud, you press a specific key a few times in succession after you power on your TNC. From those keyboard entries, the autobaud routine detects the data rate that your terminal is using and displays the TNC sign-on message to inform you that autobaud has performed its job.

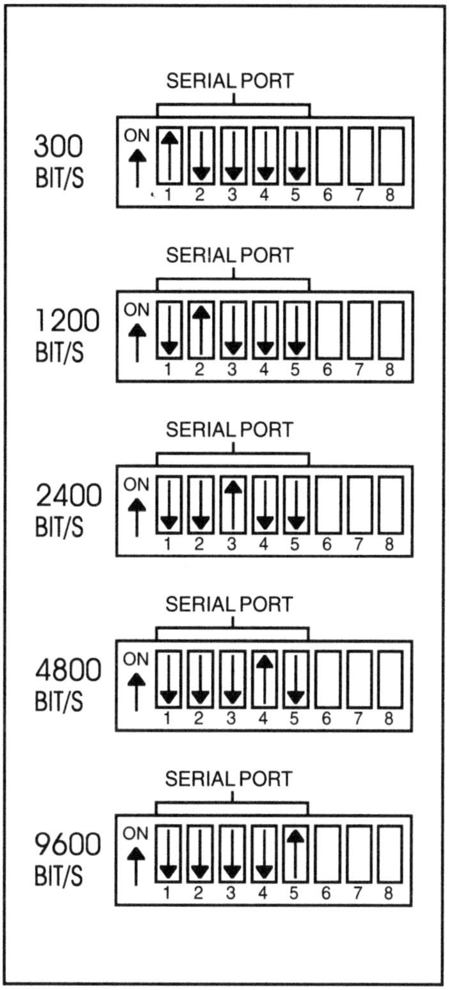

Fig 4-1—The configuration of a TNC rear-panel DIP switch for serial-port data rates of 300, 1200, 2400, 4800 and 9600 bit/s.

Radio Port Speed

The data rate of the TNC radio port is the rate used to transfer packets over the air. Below 28 MHz, 300 bit/s is used exclusively (300 bit/s is also the legal limit below 28 MHz). Above 28 MHz, 1200 bit/s is generally used. Speeds above 1200 bit/s are permitted in the VHF and UHF spectrum, and some packet-radio communication does occur at higher speeds. Unfortunately, the modems built into most TNCs are designed for 1200 bit/s. Different modulation standards are used at different data rates, so operation at higher speeds requires the addition of an external modem.

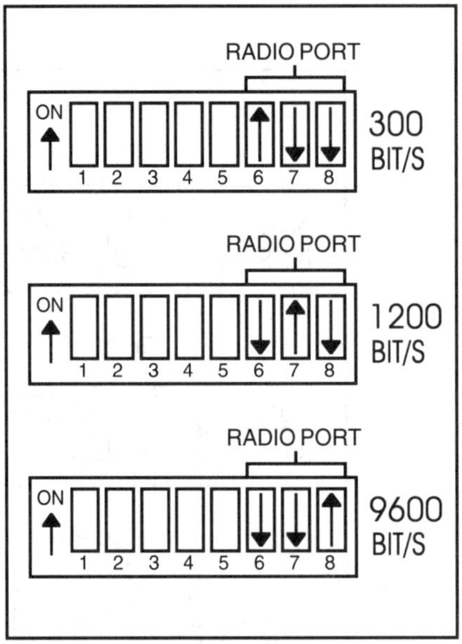

Fig 4-2—The configuration of a TNC rear-panel DIP switch for radio-port data rates of 300, 1200 and 9600 bit/s.

The radio port of some TNCs may be set to 300, 1200 or 9600 bit/s by means of a rear panel DIP switch. Fig 4-2 illustrates the position of the TNC DIP switch for each of the three data rates. You may change the radio-port data rate with your TNC turned on (as opposed to changing the serial-port data rate, when your TNC must be turned off).

Some TNCs do not use a DIP switch to set the radio port data rate. Instead, they use a software command to set this speed. Consult your TNC manual to determine how to set its radio port data rate.

Remember that you must not set the radio port data rate to anything other than 1200 bit/s, unless the internal modem of your TNC is designed for other data rates or you are using an external modem.

TURNING ON YOUR TNC

The remainder of the TNC parameters are selected by using its built-in commands. To access those commands, you must turn on your TNC.

When you power your TNC, a sign-on message similar to the display illustrated in Fig 4-3 should appear on your terminal. The message includes some or all of the following items:

1. Manufacturer and model of your TNC
2. Software used by your TNC, its version number, and revision level
3. TNC *checksum* [checksum (check summation) is the sum (in *hexadecimal*) of the bits in your TNC software in ROM; it should be equal to the checksum published in your TNC manual]
4. Amount of RAM installed in your TNC
5. Command prompt (`cmd:`) indicating that your TNC is waiting to fulfill your wishes. If the sign-on message is unreadable, turn off your TNC and check that the serial port data rate of your TNC and the data rate of your terminal are the same.

```
|A::

Tucson Amateur Packet Radio TNC-2
AX.25 Level 2 Version 2.0
Release 1.1.7   2/11/90 - 32K RAM
Checksum $51
cmd:
```

Fig 4-3—A typical TNC sign-on message, as displayed on a terminal, indicates that the TNC is functioning and is interfaced properly with its associated terminal.

COMMANDING YOUR TNC

After the sign-on message is displayed, your TNC should be in the Command Mode, as indicated by the command prompt (**cmd:**).

As of release 1.1.7 of the AX.25 Level 2, Version 2.0 software, there are 113 TNC 2 commands. Your TNC may have more if its manufacturer added special commands. Consult your TNC manual to determine if this is so.

The TNC commands may be divided into seven categories:

- Character commands, which select the special alphanumeric characters used by the TNC for various functions.
- Identification commands, which determine how a packet-radio station is identified.
- Link commands, which relate to functions and parameters used for communicating with other stations over the air.
- Monitor commands, which relate to monitoring packet-radio activity and the status of the TNC.
- Reinitialization commands, which cause the TNC to be reinitialized.
- Serial-port commands, which configure the port that is connected to your computer or terminal.
- Timing commands, which select the TNC timing parameters.

Within these seven categories, there are two types of TNC commands: *immediate commands* and *configuration commands*.

An immediate command causes your TNC to perform a task immediately. For example, the *Connect* command causes your TNC to initiate the transmission of a connect request to another station immediately after the command is invoked.

A configuration command sets a TNC parameter. For example, the *Conok* (Connect Okay) command determines how your TNC responds to connect requests from other stations. If Conok is enabled (by the command CONOK ON), your TNC accepts connect requests. If Conok is disabled (CONOK OFF), your TNC rejects connect requests.

Appendix B lists all the TNC 2 commands by category with a brief description of the function of each command. It also lists the default selection and the selectable parameters for each configuration command.

The default selection of each configuration parameter is the selection that is programmed in the permanent memory (ROM) of the TNC. When a TNC is turned on for the first time or whenever the *Reset* command is invoked, all of the configuration parameters are set to these default selections.

Each configuration parameter may be set to a user selected value. Whenever the user changes the value of any parameter (by invoking a configuration command), the new selection is stored in the temporary memory (RAM) of the TNC. When the TNC is powered off, the RAM retains the user's settings by means of a built-in battery. When the TNC is powered on again, the configuration selections are restored to the user selected values.

Entering commands is a simple matter of typing the command at the command prompt. If you are entering a configuration command, you must type a parameter after the name of the command. The command is interpreted by your TNC when you type a carriage return <CR>. Note that commands may only be entered when the command prompt (**cmd:**) is displayed by your computer or terminal. For example, to command your TNC to disconnect from a connected station, you would type DISCONNE and a carriage return at the command prompt. This operation is represented as:

cmd: DISCONNE <CR>

Another example: To configure the TNC to send the bell control character <BELL> whenever a connection is established, at the command prompt you type CBELL followed by the parameter ON and a carriage return. This operation is represented as:

cmd: CBELL ON <CR>

To save some time entering commands, most commands may be entered using one or two characters. For example, instead of typing DISCONNE for the Disconnect command, you can simply type the letter D. Similarly, instead of entering CBELL ON to enable the connection bell control character, you can type CB ON and save a few keystrokes. Note that the parameter selection OFF may be shortened to OF; the parameter selection ON is always spelled out completely as ON, however.

Throughout this book, each command will appear partially in uppercase characters and partially in lowercase characters. The uppercase portion will represent the shorthand version of the command and the uppercase and lowercase portions together will represent the longhand version of the command. For example, the Disconnect command will be represented as:

cmd: Disconne <CR>

where D is the shorthand version of the command and DISCONNE is the longhand version.

Enabling the connection bell control character would be represented as:

cmd: CBell ON <CR>

where CB is the shorthand version of the command and CBELL is the longhand version.

Note that if the command appears completely in uppercase characters, there is no shorthand version of that command. While we are on the subject of uppercase and lowercase characters, note that the TNC does not care which case you use to enter a command; uppercase or lowercase characters are acceptable.

Now that you know how to command your TNC, let's set up your TNC to suit the needs of your station equipment.

FINE TUNING THE SERIAL PORT

You communicate with your TNC through a terminal or a computer that emulates a terminal. For this discussion, both terminals and computers running software that emulate terminals will be identified as terminals. Once the correct serial port data rate is selected, your TNC is often compatible with your terminal without requiring any other changes, however, some terminals and some applications have special requirements that may be addressed using the TNC configuration commands. The following parameters are the most critical for proper terminal-to-TNC interfacing:

Echo

The *echo* function echoes keystrokes. When you type a character on the terminal keyboard, your TNC sends the same character back to be printed on the terminal display so that you can see what you have typed. The echo function is enabled by default in the TNC, based on the assumption that the terminal does not echo characters. If the terminal also provides the echo function, each character that is typed on the terminal keyboard will be printed twice on the display, because both the terminal and TNC are echoing the character. For example, if you type HI OM and the terminal prints HHII OOMM, duplicate character echoing is occurring (see Fig 4-4). If this is the case, the echo function of either your TNC or terminal should be disabled.

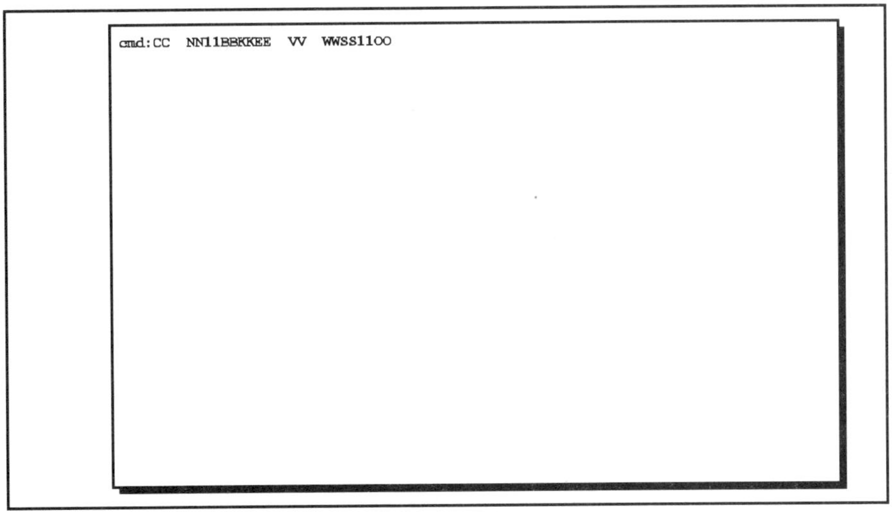

Fig 4-4—Double display of characters indicates that both the TNC and terminal are providing the echo function.

To disable the TNC echo function, at the command prompt, type:

cmd: Echo OFF <CR>

If you need to enable the echo function later, at the command prompt, type:

cmd: Echo ON <CR>

Automatic Line Feed

The *automatic line feed* function causes your TNC to send a *line feed* character <LF> to your terminal whenever it sends a carriage return character. As a result, after a carriage return is sent to the terminal, the inserted line feed causes the received characters following to be displayed on the next line of the terminal display. This function is enabled by default in the TNC because many terminals do not automatically insert line feeds after received carriage returns. If your terminal does provide the automatic line feed function, a blank line will be displayed between each line of displayed data, because the terminal is receiving two line feeds after each carriage return: one from your TNC and one from the terminal itself. If this is the case, the automatic line feed function of either your TNC or terminal should be disabled.

To disable the TNC automatic line feed function, at the command prompt, type:

cmd: AUtolf OFF <CR>

If you need to enable the automatic line feed function later, at the command prompt, type:

cmd: AUtolf ON <CR>

Character Length

Your TNC and terminal must speak the same language for successful communication. If the terminal is sending characters that are 8 bits long to the TNC while the TNC is sending characters that are 7 bits long to the terminal, there is a language barrier and communication between the two is impaired.

By default, your TNC is set for 7-bit characters or 7 *bits per character* because most terminals are capable of being configured for 7-bit characters. This TNC setting may be changed for compatibility with terminals that use 8-bit characters exclusively, or for special applications where transferring the eighth bit of the character is required. The TNC may be set for 8-bit characters, at the command prompt, by typing:

cmd: AWlen 8 <CR>

If you need to set your TNC back to the 7-bit character length later, at the command prompt, type

cmd: AWlen 7 <CR>

Parity

In a similar vein, your TNC and terminal must be using the same *parity* or communication between the two is impaired. Parity is a method of enabling a check of the accuracy of a received character by setting or resetting a bit in the transmitted character so that the sum of all of the *character bits* is even or odd depending on the type of parity in use. By default, the TNC is set for even parity because that is what most terminals use. If odd parity or no parity is required by your terminal or by some special application, the TNC may be reconfigured at the command prompt, by typing:

cmd: PARity 1 <CR>

for odd parity, and

cmd: PARity 0 <CR>

or

cmd: PARity 2 <CR>

for no parity.

To select even parity later (for example, after you connect your TNC to a terminal that uses even parity exclusively), at the command prompt, type:

cmd: PARity 3 <CR>

Screen Width

For the most intelligible terminal display, your TNC should be set for the maximum number of columns or characters that can be displayed on each line of your terminal. Since many terminals are capable of displaying 80 columns per line, the TNC is set for 80 columns per line by default. Each time the TNC sends 80 characters to the terminal, it then sends control characters that cause the terminal to begin displaying new characters received from the TNC on the next line.

If the terminal displays more or fewer than 80 columns per line, this TNC parameter may be changed at the command prompt, by typing:

cmd: Screenln *n* <CR>

where *n* is a number from 0 to 255 equal to the maximum number of columns or characters displayed per line by the terminal.

Other Serial Port Parameters

Echo, automatic line feed, screen length, character length and parity are the most critical parameters that need to be selected to make your TNC compatible with a terminal. Setting those parameters correctly should make the majority of terminals work correctly with your TNC. There are other parameters that may be selected for special applications or for terminals that require more grooming.

8bitconv strips or passes the eighth bit of characters sent by the terminal to the TNC in the Converse Mode. Eighth-bit stripping is off by default.

EScape selects either the dollar sign, $, or *escape* control character, <ESC>, as the character to be sent to the terminal from the TNC whenever the escape character is used. EScape ON selects the dollar sign; EScape OFF selects the escape character. EScape is off by default.

LCok is available for terminals that can only display uppercase characters. It enables or disables the translation of lowercase characters to uppercase before they are sent to the terminal. LCok ON enables lowercase characters. With LCok OFF, received lowercase characters are converted to uppercase before the TNC sends them to the terminal. LCok is on by default, that is, lowercase characters are not converted to uppercase for the display by the terminal.

LFIgnore causes your TNC to ignore line feeds in the Command Mode and Converse Mode, but not in the Transparent Mode. LFIgnore is on by default.

Three commands are available to compensate for terminals with slow displays requiring extra time before they start printing on a new line. This is accomplished by inserting time-consuming, but non-printing *null* control characters, <NUL>, before each new line is started. *NUcr* ON tells the TNC to send the null control character to the terminal after each carriage return; NUcr OFF disables nulls (this is the default condition). *NULf* enables or disables sending the null control character to the terminal after each line feed; it is disabled (off) by default. The *NULLS* command selects the number of null control characters to be sent when the NUcr and/or NULf functions are enabled.

Flow Control

Four commands are available to select various types of *flow control.* The flow control commands determine the way your TNC or terminal stops and starts sending characters.

When *software flow control* is selected, the transfer of characters between your terminal and TNC is stopped or restarted by the use of control characters typed at your terminal keyboard or sent from your TNC. When *hardware flow control* is selected, the transfer of characters between your terminal and TNC is controlled by TNC and terminal originated signals on the EIA terminal-to-TNC hardware interface.

Xflow selects software (*XON/XOFF*) flow control or hardware (EIA interface signal Request-to-Send) flow control. Xflow ON (the default setting) selects software flow control.

TRFlow enables or disables terminal software flow control in the Transparent Mode. With TRFlow OFF (the default setting), only hardware flow control can be used in the Transparent Mode. With TRFlow ON, the *start character* and *stop character* are used to control the flow of characters from your TNC to your terminal.

TXFlow enables or disables TNC software flow control in the Transparent Mode. TXFlow works like TRFlow; when it is OFF only hardware flow control is available. TXFlow ON allows the start and stop characters to control the flow of characters from your terminal.

Type-in flow control causes your TNC to stop sending characters to your terminal whenever a character is entered at the terminal keyboard; this prevents displayed received characters from interfering with the display of keyed characters. The *Flow* command enables or disables this function; with Flow ON (the default setting) your TNC stops sending when you are typing at your terminal.

CONTROL CHARACTERS

Thirteen commands are provided to change the values of the characters that may be used to control the interface between your terminal and TNC and to control the TNC itself. The default selection for many of the control characters is the standard ASCII value used by most terminals for control. These values may be changed, however, for terminals that use other ASCII values, or for special applications. Appendix C lists each control character available for use by your TNC, lists the command that can be invoked to change its value, and describes its function.

FINE TUNING THE RADIO PORT

The radio port of your TNC controls your transceiver, sends data for transmission to your radio, and collects audio from your radio for the TNC. There are only a few connections between the radio port and its associated radio; transmit audio, receive audio, push-to-talk (PTT) and ground connections usually are enough to allow your TNC to successfully send and receive packets through your radio.

Timing is a very important part of the success of your TNC, however. Just like a good comedian, a good TNC has to have good timing in order to get its message across. And just as a good comedian adjusts his timing to get the best response from different audiences, the timing of your TNC can be adjusted to get the message across using different parts of the radio spectrum under different operating conditions and with different equipment.

When you turn on your TNC for the first time, its timing parameters are set to default values that are optimized for VHF operation using frequency modulation (and a modern transceiver). Most packet-radio activity is on 2-meter FM, and most packet-radio operators will never use any other mode or band, so they will never have to change the TNC timing parameters. Some packet-radio operators do explore other Amateur Radio bands, however, and when they do, they have to make adjustments to their TNCs. The following paragraphs discuss the timing and timing-related parameters of your TNC that need to be adjusted for optimal operation on the various ham bands.

Data Rate

The most important timing parameter that needs adjustment when you change bands is the radio port data rate. The manner of selecting the radio-port data rate was discussed earlier in this chapter.

By default, the TNC data rate is 1200 bit/s, because this is the data rate that is used on 2-meter FM. The FCC allows 1200 bit/s operation anywhere above 28 MHz, so you may operate on 10 meters or 23 centimeters without adjusting this timing parameter. If you wish to operate below 28 MHz, however, the maximum legal data rate is 300 bit/s; this means that an adjustment of the radio-port data rate is necessary (not to mention the modification of the internal modem of the TNC or the addition of an external modem).

Above the 2-meter band, some packet-radio operators are transferring packets at higher data rates on 220 and 450 MHz. Operation at 2400, 4800, 9600 and higher is occurring successfully at these frequencies, so the radio port data rate must be adjusted upwards for compatibility. The use of an external modem is required at these higher data rates.

Receive-to-Transmit Turnaround Delay

When a transceiver transmitter is keyed, there is a slight delay before intelligence can actually be sent over the air, because various circuits in the transceiver require time to switch from the receive mode to the transmit mode. The length of this delay varies depending on the design of the transceiver. For example, transceivers using mechanical relays take longer to switch from the receive mode to the transmit mode than do transceivers using diode switching. Although the turnaround time seems instantaneous to the user, there *is* a delay. Your TNC must take this delay into consideration because it is ready to send intelligence (packets) as soon as it keys the transmitter.

By default, the receive-to-transmit turnaround delay is set to 300 ms. The turnaround delay may be adjusted at the command prompt, by typing:

cmd: TXdelay *n* <CR>

where *n* is a number from 0 to 120 representing a turnaround time in 10 ms increments. [For example, to select a delay of 360 ms, set n to 36 (360 ms / 10 ms = 36).]

If the default turnaround time is not long enough, you will have to lengthen the delay; otherwise, your TNC will not be able to send complete packets through your transceiver. It is also important to shorten the delay if the default turnaround time is too long because an overly long delay wastes valuable time on the packet-radio channel. Shortening the delay promotes more efficient packet-radio communications.

Unacknowledged Packets and Packet Length

The *MAXframe* and *Paclen* parameters are two critical TNC parameters that should be adjusted depending on operating conditions (propagation and channel activity).

MAXframe selects the maximum number of outstanding unacknowledged packets the TNC will allow at any one time. In other words, if MAXframe is set to 4, the TNC may send as many as four packets without receiving acknowledgments for any of them. Once the MAXframe limit is reached, however, the TNC will not send a new packet until one of the outstanding packets is acknowledged.

Paclen selects the maximum number of bytes of data in each packet. The TNC will never send a packet longer than the selected Paclen value. As data enters your TNC from your terminal, your TNC counts each byte of data; when the Paclen value is attained, your TNC makes up a packet containing the data, sends it over the air, and begins counting the number of bytes of data for the next packet. Your TNC will only send packets shorter than the selected Paclen value when it is specifically commanded to do so. A packet is forced whenever the *SEndpac* control character is typed (<CR> is the default SEndpac control character).

The default values for the MAXframe and Paclen parameters (4 outstanding packets each 128 bytes long) are selected for good VHF operating conditions. When you are operating on HF or when VHF operating conditions are less than optimal (there is a high level of channel activity), the MAXframe and Paclen values should be reduced as operating conditions warrant.

At 300 bit/s, it takes approximately four times as long to send the same packet as it does at 1200 bit/s. Even if you reduce the packet length by half, it still takes approximately twice as long to send a packet containing 64 bytes of data at 300 bit/s than a packet containing 128 bytes of data at 1200 bit/s. This means that your packet is on the air approximately twice as long, and the chances of it being interfered with are twice as great.

Add to this the fact that HF conditions are usually not optimal for packet-radio operation and you may end up with a lot of long unacknowledged packets hanging out there in the ether. The best thing to do is to shorten the Paclen parameter and set the MAXframe parameter to 1 to force the TNC to send one short packet, wait for an acknowledgment and then deal with the next short packet.

To change the value of the MAXframe parameter, at the command prompt, type:

cmd: MAXframe *n* <CR>

where *n* is a number from 1 to 7 representing the maximum number of outstanding unacknowledged packets.

To change the value of the Paclen parameter, at the command prompt, type:

cmd: Paclen *n* <CR>

where *n* is a number from 0 to 255 representing the maximum number of bytes of data in each packet. Note that 0 actually represents 256 bytes.

Packet Retries

When your TNC sends a packet, it waits a preset time for an acknowledgment that its packet was received without error by the intended receiving station. If the time limit is reached, your TNC again tries to obtain an acknowledgment from the receiving TNC. (The actual process of obtaining this acknowledgment is outside the scope of this chapter. If you are interested, the process is explained in Appendix A and detailed in the *AX.25 Amateur Packet-Radio Link-Layer Protocol, Version 2.0, October 1984*, available from ARRL Headquarters.) After the maximum number of retries, the sending TNC enters the disconnected state. The *FRack* parameter sets the amount of time between retries, and the *REtry* parameter controls the number of allowable retransmission attempts.

The REtry and FRack parameters should be adjusted upwards or downwards depending on operating conditions. If conditions are good (good propagation and a low level of activity on the channel), the REtry and FRack parameters may be adjusted downwards; if a packet cannot get through after one or two attempts under good conditions, there is probably an insurmountable problem with the link. For example, the intended receiving station may have gone off the air, so you might as well abandon the effort immediately.

If conditions are marginal (marginal propagation or a medium level of activity on the channel), the REtry and FRack parameters may be adjusted upwards because it may only take a little longer to get the packet through to the intended receiving station. If conditions are poor (poor propagation and/or a high level of activity on the channel), you should abandon the effort until conditions improve. You have two strikes against you: it is very difficult to get the packet through to the intended receiving station because of poor propagation, and your packets are likely to collide with other packets because of the crowded channel.

By default, the REtry parameter value is set to 10 retries, but that may be changed at the command prompt, by typing:

cmd: REtry *n* <CR>

where n is a number from 0 to 15. Zero represents an infinite number of retries and 1 to 15 represents the maximum number of retries that will be attempted before the TNC stops repeating a packet. Note that the REtry parameter does not include the initial transmission of the packet; it only represents the number of retries after the initial packet transmission.

By default, the FRack parameter value is set to 3 seconds, but this may be changed at the command prompt, by typing:

cmd: FRack *n* <CR>

where *n* is a number from 1 to 15 representing the number of seconds that your TNC will wait for a packet acknowledgment before it again tries to obtain an acknowledgment. Note that your TNC automatically adjusts this value higher depending on the number of digipeaters used in the selected path of the packet according to the formula:

$$\textbf{FRack} \times (2 \times dr + 1) = \textbf{adjusted FRack}$$

where *dr* is the number of digipeaters in the selected path. [For example, if FRack is set to 4 seconds and 2 digipeaters are in the selected path, the adjusted FRack value is 20 seconds (4 sec × (2 × 2 digipeaters + 1)) = 20 sec).]

Prioritized Acknowledgment

TNCs that are compatible with AX.25 Level 2, Version 2.0 release 1.1.7 or later are capable of using the channel-sharing protocol called *prioritized acknowledgment.* As its name implies, this protocol gives priority to packet acknowledgments (ACKs) on a channel.

An ACK indicates that a packet has been received correctly. By giving an ACK priority, the station that sent the packet will receive the ACK more quickly and, as a result, be less likely to resend the packet. On channels where ACKs are not given priority, ACKs may be delayed long enough to cause the waiting station to give up and resend the packet, thus wasting precious time on the channel.

Configuring a TNC for prioritized acknowledgment involves setting the parameters as indicated in Table 4-1.

These settings are recommended as a starting point. Once you are on the air, you may have to adjust them as conditions warrant. Also, check your TNC manual in case it recommends different settings.

Digipeater Timing

When your TNC sends a packet, it knows that the packet was received successfully upon receiving an acknowledgment (ACK). When a digipeater and some network nodes send a packet, they never know if the packet was received successfully because they don't wait for an acknowledgment. Acknowledgments, if any, are relayed by the digipeater or node back to the station originating the packet. If no ACK is relayed back, the originating station knows there was a packet failure and must act accordingly.

Table 4-1

TNC Configuration for Prioritized Acknowledgment

Parameter	*1200 bit/s VHF FM*	*300 bit/s HF*
ACkprior	ON	ON
ACKTime	14	52
DEAdtime	33	8
DWait	33	8
FRack	8	16
MAXframe	don't care	1
Paclen	don't care	32 - 128
RESptime	0	0
SLots	3	3

To compensate for the digipeater or node lack of acknowledgment (or LACK), a timing parameter is included in your TNC to give digipeated packets a break. When a TNC is digipeating packets, it sends its packets as soon as the channel is clear of activity. If a TNC is originating its own packets, however, it waits a selected time period (set by the *DWait* command) after the channel is clear before it sends its packets. As a result, when a channel is clear, the digipeater *always* transmits first. This reduces the chance of digipeated packets colliding with non-digipeated TNC packets.

The default setting of the DWait parameter is 16, which represents 160 ms. To change this timing parameter at the command prompt, type:

cmd: DWait *n* <CR>

where *n* is a number from 0 to 250 representing a delay in 10 ms increments. For example, to select a delay of 120 ms, set n to 12 (120 ms / 10 ms = 12).

To work effectively, all of the TNCs on a channel used by one or more digipeaters or network nodes should be using the same DWait value. Unless you know that the packet radio operators in your area are using a DWait value other than the default, you should leave your TNC set at the default value.

Voice Repeater Timing

If you plan to use a voice FM repeater for relaying your packet-radio transmissions, there are two TNC timing parameters that can be adjusted for optimal voice repeater operation. *AXDelay* inserts a delay between the time your transmitter is keyed and the time a packet is actually sent. AXdelay is used to allow the voice repeater to be keyed up and ready to relay your transmitted packet (this delay is in addition to the TXdelay mentioned earlier). Voice FM repeater packet radio operation is not common, so AXDelay is set to 0 ms by default. If you need to use a voice repeater for packet, a delay may be selected at the command prompt, by typing:

cmd: AXDelay *n* <CR>

where *n* is a number from 0 to 180 representing a delay in 10 ms increments. For example, to select a delay of 480 ms, set n to 48 (480 ms / 10 ms = 48).

Most voice repeaters continue transmitting unmodulated carrier for a certain amount of time after each repeated transmission to indicate to the repeated station that the repeater is functioning. This delay is called the *hang time* and may be used in conjunction with the *AXHang* command to speed up voice repeater packet-radio operation.

If the TNC is ready to send a packet and channel activity has been detected within the selected AXHang parameter value, the TNC keys its transmitter (keeping the repeater keyed) and sends data after the TXdelay parameter value has expired. This saves time, because the TNC does not wait for the AXdelay time.

Again, voice FM repeater packet-radio operation is not common, so AXHang is set to 0 ms by default. If you need to use an FM voice repeater, AXHang timing may be selected, at the command prompt, by typing:

cmd: AXHang *n* <CR>

where *n* is a number from 0 to 20 representing a hang time in 100 ms increments. For example, to select a hang time of 1200 ms in a TNC 2, set n to 12 (1200 ms / 100 ms = 12).

How do you select the correct values for AXDelay and AXHang? In most cases, you do not know the length of a voice repeater key-up delay and hang time, so unless another local packet-radio operator has already determined the best values for AXDelay and AXHang, you will have to experiment until you determine the appropriate values.

We've reviewed the most critical TNC timing and timing-related parameters that you need to check before you put your TNC on the air. Refer to Appendix B for other timing command parameters. Now, there is only one more thing left to do.

STATION IDENTIFICATION

One last TNC parameter needs to be set, the call sign that identifies your station. To enter the call sign, at the command prompt, type:

cmd: MYcall *x* <CR>

where *x* is the call sign of your station.

In packet radio, one Amateur Radio operator may have more than one packet radio station on the air at the same time. A packet radio operator may run a full-time network node, a packet radio bulletin board system and his own packet radio station. To differentiate these stations, the AX.25 protocol provides a *Secondary Station Identifier* (*SSID*), which is a number (0 to 15) that is appended to the call sign with a hyphen. For example, my home station might be identified as WA1LOU-0, my packet-radio bulletin board system as WA1LOU-4 and my network node as WA1LOU-5. To enter the SSID in the TNC, use the MYcall command. For example, to enter my network node call sign in the TNC, at the command prompt, I type

cmd: MYcall WA1LOU-5 <CR>.

Note that if a call sign is entered without an SSID, the TNC assumes that the SSID is 0.

BEFORE YOU BEGIN

Before you begin selecting parameters in a new TNC or a reinitialized TNC, you should set your terminal for compatibility with the default selections for serial port baud of the TNC, character length (bits per character), and parity. Typically, 1200 bit/s, 7 bit characters and even parity are the defaults of the TNC. If you do not do this, you will not be able to communicate with your TNC!

If you are working with a TNC whose serial port data rate is selected by means of a rear panel DIP switch, there is no default data rate, so, set the switch for 1200 bit/s (see Fig 4-1). If the serial port data rate of the TNC is software selectable, the default data rate is likely to be 1200 bit/s, but check the TNC manual to see if this is so. If it is not 1200 bit/s, then set your terminal data rate equal to the TNC default serial port data rate.

After the terminal and TNC are compatible, power up the TNC and its preamble should be displayed at your terminal in plain English (see Fig 4-3). To change the serial port data rate, character length, and/or parity of the TNC and terminal, do so by changing the setting of the TNC first, then change the setting of the terminal one parameter at a time. For example, to change the serial port data rate to 9600 bit/s, the character length to 8 bits, and the parity to no parity, you would proceed according to the following steps:

1. Set your TNC for 8 character bits.
2. Set your terminal for 8 character bits.
3. Set your TNC for no parity.
4. Set your terminal for no parity.
5. Set your TNC for 9600 bit/s.
6. Set your terminal for 9600 bit/s.

Now, you can proceed to change any other of the TNC parameters as you desire.

AFTER YOU ARE FINISHED

That concludes the configuration of the TNC. It is now ready to launch its first packet. The next chapter will check out your TNC and make sure it is ready for prime time packet radio.

5

Testing

DOES IT WORK?

One of the best ways to find out if your installation works is to give it a test under fire. FCC regulations permit Amateur Radio operators to test their equipment on the air, so try connecting to yourself through a local station and sending some test data (*the quick brown fox* works just as well on packet radio as it does on RTTY).

To connect to yourself, the other station you are connecting through must have its digipeater function enabled. The digipeater function is enabled by default. If it is disabled, it can be enabled at the command prompt by typing:

cmd: DIGipeat ON <CR>

Once the other station has the digipeater function enabled, you can connect to yourself at the command prompt, by typing:

cmd: *URCALL* Via *THRCAL* <CR>

where *URCALL* is the call sign of your station and *THRCAL* is the call sign of the station through which you are digipeating.

If you are able to connect with yourself and successfully receive the test data, your installation is working. Go to the next section of this book and have fun!

If you are unable to connect with yourself (or worse), read further for the possible solution to the problem.

TROUBLESHOOTING YOUR TNC

You don't have to be a rocket scientist to figure out why your TNC is not working. All you need is a little help from your friendly TNC troubleshooting guide, which is presented in Table 5-1.

Table 5-1
TNC Troubleshooting Guide

Trouble	*Possible Causes*
Nothing happens after turning on the TNC power switch.	Power source problem; check connection between TNC and power supply; check that connection is tight; check connection wiring; check that an external switch (such as a wall switch) that controls the power supply is not turned off.
No sign-on message after power-up; front panel indicators are lit.	Connection between TNC and terminal; check that connection is tight; check the Received Data (pin 3) and Signal Ground (pin 7) leads.
Sign-on message is garbled.	Incompatibility between TNC and terminal; check that the serial port data rate, parity and character bit length of the TNC and terminal are equal.
TNC does not respond to keyboard input.	Connection between TNC and terminal; check that connection is tight; check the Transmitted Data (pin 2) and Signal Ground (pin 7) leads.
Cannot copy packets from other stations; DCD front panel indicator does not light when signal is heard.	Connection between TNC and radio; check that connection is tight; check the connection between the TNC audio input and radio audio output. Receiver audio is set too low; turn up the volume.
Cannot copy packets from other stations; DCD front panel indicator lights when signal is heard.	Connection between TNC and terminal; check that connection is tight; check the Received Data lead, pin 3. Receiver audio is set too high; turn down the volume.
Cannot copy packets from other stations; DCD front panel indicator lights when signal is heard; garbled characters appear on terminal display.	Incompatibility between TNC and channel activity. Check that the radio port data rate, parity and character bit length of the TNC and other stations on the air are equal.
Transmitter does not key although PTT indicator lights.	Connection between TNC and radio; check that connection is tight; check the PTT and ground leads.
Transmitter is keyed continuously.	Connection between TNC and radio; check that connection is tight; check the PTT and ground leads.
Other stations cannot copy your packets, but you can copy their packets.	Connection between TNC and radio; check that connection is tight; check the connection between the TNC audio output and radio audio input.
	TNC audio output is set incorrectly. Check deviation.
	TX delay is set too low. Increase TXdelay by 10 ms increments.

Assuming that your TNC is functioning properly, that is, it was not dead on arrival or is not on the verge of death, then this troubleshooting guide will be able to diagnose the majority of problems that you are likely to encounter with your TNC installation.

If your packet radio controller is a multiport and/or multimode controller, that adds complexity to troubleshooting your installation, complexity that is not covered by the guide. If the troubleshooting guide is unable to solve the problem in a multiport and/or multimode environment, then check that the problem is not related to selecting the incorrect port or incorrect mode. Your equipment manual may offer some assistance.

Internal Diagnostics

Some TNCs provide their own self-contained diagnostics. Check the TNC manual to find out what, if anything, is available and, if all else fails, try them.

Deviation

In the FM mode, frequency information is encoded by varying the carrier frequency of the FM signal, while amplitude is encoded by controlling the amount that the carrier frequency is varied or deviated. This change, shift or *deviation* of the carrier frequency is proportional to the amplitude of the input signal. If the amplitude of the input signal is zero, there will be no change (no deviation) in the carrier frequency and there will be nothing heard in the receiver at the other end. As the amplitude of the input signal increases, the amount by which the carrier shifts (or deviates) increases, too.

For this explanation, let us assume that each volt of amplitude corresponds to 1 kHz of deviation. Therefore, if you modulate a 1500 Hz tone at a carrier frequency of 147.000 MHz with 2 volts of amplitude, the carrier will deviate 2 kHz, that is, between 146.999 and 147.001 MHz. If you modulate the same tone at the same carrier frequency with 4 volts of amplitude, the carrier will deviate 4 kHz (between 146.998 and 147.002 MHz).

Ideally, the deviation of your signal should fall between 3.0 and 4.5 kHz. It will be hard to decode your packets if your signal is below 3.0 kHz of deviation. The TNC at the other end cannot decode your packets if it can't hear them! On the other hand, it will be difficult to decode your packets if your deviation is above 4.5 kHz. Your transmitter can not deviate signals much higher than 4.5 kHz. Too high a deviation causes your signal to be clipped by the audio stages of your transmitter and results in a distorted signal in the receiver at the other end of the connection, that is, a signal that a TNC will have a tough time decoding.

To achieve the best throughput of your packets, you must set your FM signal deviation within the ideal range. To do this, you need a deviation meter and a alignment tool that will allow you to adjust the audio output level control of your TNC.

To check the deviation of your transmitter, connect it to a dummy load and start transmitting a dead carrier, that is, without audio input, while you attempt to tune in your signal with the deviation meter. If the meter has a speaker output, I recommend attaching a speaker to it to simplify the tuning procedure. With a speaker attached, you simply tune the meter until you hear the squelch break, then you continue tuning very slowly until you tune to the center of the signal.

Next, you put your TNC in the calibration mode by typing at the command prompt:

cmd: CALibra ON <CR>

In the calibration mode, check the deviation as you transmit, in succession, the high and low frequency tones of the TNC (pressing your keyboard Space Bar switches between the high and low tones). If the deviation of a tone is too high or too low, adjust the level accordingly using the TNC audio output control. The location and accessibility of the audio output control varies with each TNC. Check your TNC manual for its location.

If your TNC does not have such a control, you will have to adjust the microphone gain of your transmitter. If that is the case, check the radio manual for the location and accessibility of that control. After you adjust the audio output control, check both tones again to make sure they are still adjusted correctly.

Applications

Section 3

Packet radio…it is an effective form of telecommunications, but what can you do with it? The following chapters describe how packet radio is being used throughout the Amateur Radio world.

It's child's play! Learn a few commands and you can experience the new adventure called packet radio—as are the author's daughter, Hayley, and XYL, Laurie. ***(WA1LOU photo)***

6

Basic Operation

Some packet radio operating procedures are very similar to procedures used in other modes, but some are very different. In this chapter, we'll explore those similarities and differences.

COMMAND, CONVERSE AND TRANSPARENT MODES

Before we can talk about establishing a contact, we should discuss the various operating modes of a TNC. A TNC has three operating modes: the command, converse and transparent modes.

The *command mode* is the TNC state that allows the user to configure and control the TNC, while the converse and transparent modes are the TNC states in which packet radio communication actually occurs. In the command mode, the TNC sends the command prompt to the terminal to indicate that it is ready to accept user commands that configure TNC parameters and control TNC functions. In the converse and transparent modes, the user sends and receives messages and files to and from other packet radio stations.

So then, what's the difference between the converse mode and the transparent mode?

The *converse mode* is intended for most packet radio communications. When you are in converse mode, most of what you type is sent as data to another station, while special characters may be interspersed in that data to command your TNC to perform a variety of functions. For example, to send a packet in the converse mode, you simply enter the text you wish to send followed by the *Sendpac* character (by default, this is a carriage return, <CR>). The text is transmitted to the other station, but the Sendpac character is not sent. This can be a drawback if you wish to send these special characters to the other station (and not have them interpreted as commands by your TNC).

The solution to this problem is the *transparent mode*. In the transparent mode, no characters (with one exception) are interpreted as commands by your TNC. As a result, any character can be imbedded in the data intended for transmission except for a single special character, which is used to switch the TNC back to command mode. Even this character may be sent to the other station in the transparent mode because it must be typed three times in a row (and within a certain time frame) before it causes the TNC to switch modes. Thus, in the transparent mode, any data can be sent by the TNC.

To transfer the TNC to the transparent mode, at the command prompt, type:

cmd: Trans <CR>

and to transfer the TNC to the converse mode, at the command prompt, type:

cmd: CONVers <CR>

MAKING A CONTACT

In all modes of Amateur Radio communications, you must establish contact with another station before you can initiate communications. In packet radio, you connect to or make a connection with another station before you can initiate communications. To make a connection, you command the TNC to do so by using the *Connect* command, at the command prompt, by typing:

cmd: Connect *WA1LOU* <CR>

where *WA1LOU* is the call sign of the station you wish to contact.

After you type the Connect command, the TNC sends connect request packets to the desired station. The TNC also switches to the converse mode, the transparent mode or remains in the command mode depending on the selection of the *Newmode* parameter.

Newmode determines how the TNC acts when the Connect command is invoked and when a connection is ended. If Newmode is enabled (the default selection), the TNC switches to the converse mode or transparent mode after the Connect command is invoked and switches back to the command mode after a connection is ended. If Newmode is disabled, the TNC remains in the command mode until a connection is established (it then switches to converse or transparent mode) and the TNC does not switch to the command mode when a connection is ended. To enable or disable Newmode at the command prompt, type:

cmd: NEwmode *x* <CR>

where *x* is ON to enable the Newmode function or OFF to disable it.

With Newmode enabled, you may begin typing your first message to the station you wish to contact while the TNC is still trying to establish a connection with that station. If Newmode is disabled, you cannot enter your first message until a connection is actually established. (Refer to Fig 6-1 for an illustration of the difference between enabled and disabled Newmode.)

The mode the TNC enters after the Connect command is invoked or after a connection is established is determined by the *Conmode* parameter. The TNC switches to the converse mode by default, but this may be changed, at the command prompt, by typing:

cmd: CONMode TRans <CR>

to cause the TNC to switch to the transparent mode. To select the converse mode again, at the command prompt, type:

cmd: CONMode COnvers <CR>

The TNC will attempt to make a connection (send connect requests) until an inter-

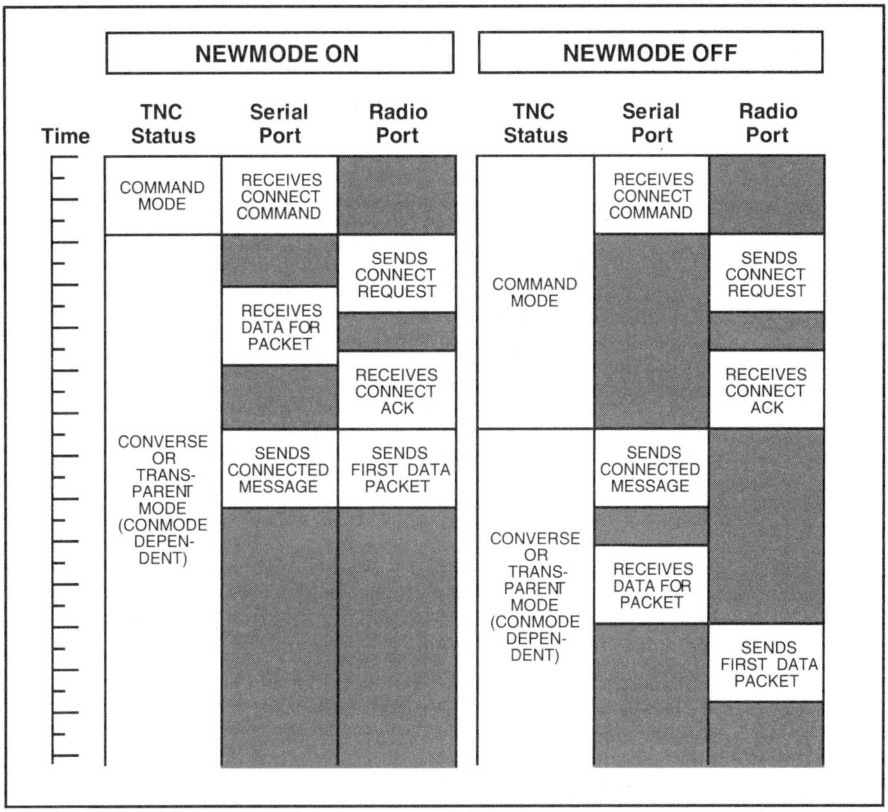

Fig 6-1— Enabling and disabling *Newmode* causes the TNC to operate very differently; when Newmode is enabled, communications can be initiated more quickly.

nal counter reaches 1 + the Retry parameter; the TNC then displays the "retry count exceeded" message, and enters the disconnected state.

If your terminal displays:

***** retry count exceeded**

***** DISCONNECTED**

This means that the TNC was unable to make a connection with the addressed station.

If a connection is not established with the addressed station and your terminal displays:

***** WA1LOU busy**

***** DISCONNECTED**

This means that the TNC has received a frame from the addressed station indicating that it is busy. The addressed station may already be connected to another station (with its multiple connect function disabled) or the addressed station may be configured to reject connect requests (the Conok parameter is OFF).

If a connection is established with the addressed station, your terminal displays:

***** CONNECTED to *WA1LOU***

where *WA1LOU* is the call sign of the addressed station.

IT'S ALWAYS YOUR TURN TO TRANSMIT

Once a contact is established and communication begins, there are standard procedures to indicate that you are finished transmitting and ready to receive a transmission from the other station. The letter K is used in CW communications and the word "over" is used in voice communications. In packet radio, however, the situation is a bit different, because packet radio communication is virtually full duplex.

When you are using landline telephone equipment (which is a full-duplex system), you don't need to say "over" to let the parties on the other end of the line know that it is their turn to talk; both parties can talk at the same time if they want to. When you send a transmission via packet radio, you do not need to let the other station know it is the other station's turn to transmit. The other station has probably sent a packet back to you already!

In other Amateur Radio modes, communications are half duplex; at any one time, one station transmits while the other station receives. In packet radio, transmissions are very short, therefore, connected stations are in the receive mode most of the time. In the receive mode, you are often typing a response to the other station's previous transmission. When you enter a carriage return, your thoughts are transmitted and the other station's next transmission is displayed on your terminal awaiting your next response.

This is almost full-duplex communication (packets can be traveling in both directions at once, and sometimes are!). As a result, you do not usually need to indicate when you are finished transmitting and are ready to receive the other station's transmission.

Old habits die hard, however, and you will see some stations using K from the CW mode or a string of greater-than signs (>>>) to indicate the end of a transmission. There is nothing wrong or illegal about using such indicators, but they are usually unnecessary in a packet radio contact. However, if a single packet is not a complete transmission and the packet radio contact is getting confusing, don't be afraid to use some sort of end-of-transmission indicator if it helps you communicate.

BREAKING A CONNECTION

To complete a contact on most Amateur Radio modes, you simply say "73" or "see you later" and call another station, call CQ or turn off the transceiver. In packet radio, one more step is required. After all of the good-byes are exchanged, your TNC is still connected to the other station's TNC. You or the operator at the other station must command the TNC to break this connection by invoking the *Disconnect* command. This poses a problem; to use the disconnect command, the TNC must be in the command mode, but ever since the connection was established, the TNC has either been in the converse mode or the transparent mode. The solution is to switch back to the command mode.

In the converse mode, simply enter the *command mode character*, which is <CTRL-C> by default. After the command mode character is entered, the TNC enters the command mode and the command prompt is displayed at the terminal.

In the transparent mode, the command mode character must be entered three times in succession, in a timely manner according to the value of the *Cmdtime* parameter (one second is the default value for the Cmdtime parameter). To transfer from the transparent mode to the command mode, you must use the following sequence:

1) After the last keyboard entry, do not type anything for a time period that is *greater* than the Cmdtime parameter (1 second, by default).

2) Enter the command mode character <CTRL-C> three times in succession with the time between each entry being *less* than the Cmdtime parameter (1 second, by default).

3) Again, do not type anything for a time period that is *greater* than the Cmdtime parameter (1 second, by default) and the command prompt will be displayed at your terminal.

Once the command prompt is displayed, invoke the Disconnect command by typing:

cmd: Disconne <CR>

When the disconnection is completed, the terminal displays:

***** DISCONNECTED**

and the TNC does or does not enter the command mode depending on the selection of the Newmode parameter described earlier.

Note that you may change the command mode character at the command prompt, by typing:

cmd: COMmand *n* <CR>

where *n* is the hexadecimal or decimal value of the ASCII character selected to represent the command mode character (refer to Appendix G, ASCII Character Set, for the hexadecimal and decimal values of each ASCII character).

You can also change the Cmdtime parameter at the command prompt, by typing:

cmd: CMdtime *n* <CR>

where *n* is a number from 0 to 250 representing the transparent mode time-out value in 1-second increments.

MONITORING PACKET RADIO ACTIVITY

The TNC is a versatile monitor. In other modes of Amateur Radio communications, you limit reception by the judicious use of filters and related circuits that are built into your receiver. Even the best filters cannot block out very strong signals only a few kilohertz away from your operating frequency. A TNC, however, can be configured to reject signals from your next door packet radio neighbor operating on the same frequency you're using!

Do you want to know what other stations are on frequency? In other modes of Amateur Radio, you would have to sit by the receiver and compile a list of the stations you hear on the frequency. In packet radio, your TNC can provide you with a list of the stations monitored on frequency and can tell you at what time they were monitored as well.

A variety of monitoring commands are provided to configure the TNC to your monitoring requirements. (Refer to Table 6-1 to see how the various monitoring commands affect the display of monitored packets.) The most important monitoring command is aptly named the *Monitor* command! This determines whether or not your terminal displays received packets while the TNC is in the command mode. By default, the monitoring function is enabled. This may be changed, however, at the command prompt, by typing:

Table 6-1
Monitor Commands

Display	*Monitor*	*MRpt*	*MStamp*	*DAYUsa*	*HEaderln*
WA1LOU>N1QDA-2: Hello!	ON	off	off	ON	off
WA1LOU>N1QDA-2,NODE1,NODE2*: Hello!	ON	ON	off	ON	off
WA1LOU>N1QDA-2,NODE1,NODE2* [03/08/96 07:35:11]: Hello!	ON	ON	ON	ON	off
WA1LOU>N1QDA-2,NODE1,NODE2* [08-03-96 07:35:11]: Hello!	ON	ON	ON	off	off
WA1LOU>N1QDA-2,NODE1,NODE2* [08-03-96 07:35:11]: Hello!	ON	ON	ON	ON	ON

cmd: Monitor *x* <CR>

where *x* is ON to enable the monitoring function or OFF to disable the monitoring function.

If the monitoring function is enabled, received packets are displayed in the following format:

WA1LOU>N1QDA-2: Hello!

where *WA1LOU-0* is the station originating the packet (0 SSIDs are not displayed), *N1QDA-2* is the station of destination for the packet, and *Hello!* is the data contained in the packet. The originating and receiving call signs are separated by the greater-than sign (>), and the call signs and data are separated by a colon (:).

Monitoring While Connected

The monitoring function only allows you to monitor packets while the TNC is in the command mode. When your station is connected to another station, your TNC will usually only display packets from the station to which you are connected. If you need to know what is going on among other stations on the frequency while you are connected to another station, use the *Mcon* command to enable the TNC to continue monitoring other channel activity during a connection. By default, the Mcon function is disabled, but this may be changed at the command prompt, by typing:

cmd: MCon *x* <CR>

where *x* is ON to enable the Mcon function or OFF to disable the Mcon function.

Network Node Pathfinding

If network nodes (or digipeaters) are used for passing packets in your area, it is often useful to know what node and digipeater paths are being used. The *Mrpt* command enables the TNC to display the call signs of the nodes and digipeaters used by each monitored packet. By default, the Mrpt function is enabled. This may be changed, at the command prompt, by typing:

cmd: MRpt *x* <CR>

where *x* is ON to enable the MRpt function or OFF to disable the MRpt function.

If the Mrpt function is enabled, received packets are displayed in the following format:

WA1LOU>N1QDA-2,NODE1,NODE2*: Hello!

where *WA1LOU* is the station originating the packet, *N1QDA-2* is the station of destination for the packet, and *Hello!* is the data contained in the packet. *NODE1* and *NODE2* are nodes used to pass packets between WA1LOU and N1QDA-2. The asterisk (*) after NODE2 indicates that NODE2 is the node that is actually being received by your TNC.

Time-Stamped Monitoring

It is often useful to know when a packet was actually monitored. This is especially true if you "read the mail" later (by reading a printout or a saved file of monitored packets). Your TNC has a clock that can be used to *time stamp* monitored packets. Before time stamping can be used, however, the TNC clock must be set using the *Daytime* command. To set the TNC clock, at the command prompt, type:

cmd: DAytime *yymmddhhmm* <CR>

where *yy* is the last two digits of the year, *mm* is the numerical representation of the month (01 through 12), *dd* is the day of the month (01 through 31), *hh* is the hour of the day (00 through 23), and the second *mm* is the minute of the hour (00 through 59). For example, to set the TNC clock to August 11, 1996, 1:36 PM, at the command prompt, type:

cmd: DAytime 9608111336 <CR>

where 96 represents the year; 08, the month; 11, the day of the month; 13, the hour of the day, and 36, the minute of the hour.

After you have set the TNC clock, you may check the time, at the command prompt, by typing:

cmd: DAytime <CR>

The date and time is displayed in the following format: 08/11/96 13:36:00 for August 11, 1996, 1:36 PM.

If you prefer to have the date displayed in the European format with the day of the month preceding the month (11-8-96), rather than in the American format, where the day of the month follows the month (8/11/96), the *Dayusa* function must be disabled (by default, the function is enabled). To change the Dayusa function, at the command prompt, type:

cmd: DAYUsa *x* <CR>

where *x* is ON to enable the Dayusa function or OFF to disable the Dayusa function.

Please note that the TNC clock is not intended to be an accurate timepiece. In most TNCs, it loses time. This loss of time can be compensated for by using the *Clkadj* command to insert a correction factor in the TNC clock routine. The value of the correction factor must be determined by experimentation. Try different values until you find one that provides the best clock accuracy. By default, the correction factor is 0; to insert a correction factor, at the command prompt, type:

cmd: CLKADJ *n* <CR>

where *n* is a number between 0 and 65535 representing the TNC clock correction factor.

Now that the TNC clock is set, we can put it to use. The *Mstamp* command controls the time stamping of monitored packets. Time stamping of monitored packets is disabled by default; this may be changed, at the command prompt, by typing:

cmd: MStamp *x* <CR>

where *x* is ON to enable the time stamping of monitored packets or OFF to disable this feature. When time stamping is enabled, monitored packets are displayed in the following format:

WA1LOU>N1QDA-2 [03/08/96 07:35:11]: Hello!

with the date and time that the packet was received displayed between a set of brackets preceding the colon (:) and the data portion of the packet.

With the call signs of the originating, destination and node/digipeater stations and the date and time being displayed along with the data contained in each packet, the length of a displayed packet often extends to a second line. To make the display more legible, the packet *header* (the call signs, date and time) may be displayed on one line with the data on the line immediately following the header. This function is enabled by means of the *Headerln* command, which is disabled by default. To change this, at the command prompt, type:

cmd: HEaderln *x* <CR>

where *x* is ON to enable the separate-line display of packet headers and data or OFF to disable the separate-line display function. After Headerln is enabled, the previous example of a monitored packet is displayed as:

WA1LOU>N1QDA-2 [03/08/96 07:35:11]:

Hello!

The TNC clock can also be used to time stamp connection messages. By default, this time stamping function is disabled. This may be changed, at the command prompt, by typing:

cmd: CONStamp *x* <CR>

where *x* is ON to enable the time stamping of connection messages or OFF to disable the time stamping. When this function is enabled, connection messages are displayed in the following format:

***** CONNECTED to WA1LOU [03/08/96 12:34:56]**

where the date and time that the connection was made is displayed between a set of brackets that follows the connection message.

Log of Monitored Stations

Do you wish to know which stations have been active on the frequency lately? The *Mheard* command allows you to obtain a list of the most recent 18 stations monitored by the TNC. To obtain this list, at the command prompt, type:

cmd: MHeard <CR>

and the last 18 different stations monitored are displayed in the following format:

VE3NEC* 09/01/95 16:29:24

N1HUI-6*09/01/95 16:29:23

N1OPO-15* 09/01/95 16:29:17

WA2JNF-4* 09/01/95 16:27:13

N1RHN-15* 09/01/95 16:25:05

N2FFA* 09/01/95 16:18:27

W1GTT09/01/95 16:18:22

W2ZQ*09/01/95 16:16:12

W2HOB-15* 09/01/95 16:16:03

N2LZX* 09/01/95 16:14:35

SWNH 09/01/95 16:09:10

VE2JOR* 09/01/95 16:09:08

N3MQV* 09/01/95 16:08:14

N2UNH* 09/01/95 16:07:34

N1QDA09/01/95 16:03:51

WO2J*09/01/95 16:03:27

N2MSM-14* 09/01/95 15:50:48

N1FZE09/01/95 15:44:07

where the asterisk (*) after a station indicates that that station was monitored through a node or digipeater. The date and time are displayed only if the TNC clock has been set.

In order to start a new list, the old list of monitored stations logged by the TNC may be deleted. This is accomplished by invoking the *Mhclear* command, at the command prompt, by typing:

cmd: MHClear <CR>

Discriminatory Monitoring

The *Lcalls* command is used in conjunction with the *Budlist* command to permit the TNC to limit station monitoring. These commands may be used to limit monitoring exclusively to certain stations or to limit monitoring to exclude certain stations. For example, this Lcalls-Budlist combination is useful in eliminating the display of beacons that constantly bombard your TNC from certain stations. It is also useful to eliminate the display of messages from PBBSs that are being read for the umpteenth time. As many as eight stations can be selected or excluded in this way.

First, the call signs (and SSIDs) of the stations to be limited are entered into the TNC with the Lcalls command, at the command prompt, by typing:

cmd: LCAlls *STN1*, ... *STN8* <CR>

where *STN1* through *STN8* represent the call signs of one to eight stations to be limited (the call signs must be separated by commas).

Next, the Budlist command is used to select the desired discriminatory monitoring. Budlist is disabled by default and packets from stations included in the Lcalls list are *not* displayed. On the other hand, if Budlist is enabled, only the packets from the stations included in the Lcalls list are displayed. To change the status of the Budlist function, at the command prompt, type:

cmd: BUdlist *x* <CR>

where *x* is ON to enable the Budlist function or OFF to disable the function.

If no calls are entered in the Lcalls list, the status of Budlist is inconsequential and the packets of all monitored stations are displayed. To check the Lcalls list, at the command prompt, type:

cmd: LCAlls <CR>

and the Lcalls station list is displayed.

Other Monitoring Functions

Other on-the-air monitoring commands include the *Null* command, which, when enabled, causes the TNC to display *unconnected packets* as well as connected packets. (Unconnected packets are used when more than two packet radio stations are in communication with each other, or for CQs and beacon messages.) The *Mcom* command, when enabled, causes the TNC to display connect, disconnect, UA, and DM frames in addition to I (information) frames. Finally, the *Mfilter* command can be used to specify as many as four ASCII characters that are then filtered from monitored packets (in order to eliminate certain control characters that can disrupt your terminal's operation).

MONITORING THE TNC

Besides on-the-air monitoring, there is a class of monitoring commands that are concerned with monitoring the status of the TNC. The most frequently used command of this class is the *Display* command, which causes the terminal to display the status of all selectable TNC parameters. Since over a hundred different parameters may be displayed using this command, it is made more useful by optionally limiting the display of parameters to a certain class of parameters, such as timing parameters. To invoke this command, at the command prompt, type:

cmd: DISPlay *x* <CR>

where *x* may be optionally included to limit the display of parameters to a certain class, as follows: *A* for asynchronous port parameters, *C* for special characters, *H* for health counters and TNC front panel indicators, *I* for identification parameters, *L* for link parameters, *M* for monitor parameters and *T* for timing parameters.

In addition to the Display command, there is a group of esoteric TNC monitoring commands that allow you to display such things as the number of frames discarded because of length or bad CRC. These monitoring commands are listed in Appendix B.

MULTIPLE CONNECTIONS

Your TNC can be connected with more than one station simultaneously. In fact, it may be connected with as many as ten other stations at the same time! Multiple connection capability was intended for such uses as traffic handling, roundtable communicating and multiple-user PBBS operation. Use your imagination and you probably can discover a new use for the multiple connection function.

One way of describing how multiple connections work is to think of your TNC as having ten channels or *streams* for the flow of data. The streams are labeled A through J, and instead of using a front panel channel selector to choose a stream, you command the TNC to select a stream for you.

You can limit the number of streams that can be used for multiple connections to any number between one and ten (if only one stream is available for use, you have effectively disabled the multiple connection function). One available stream is the default selection. To enable the multiconnect function, at the command prompt, type:

cmd: USers *n* <CR>

where *n* is a number between 1 and 10 representing the number of channels to be made available for communications (*n* must be greater than 1 to enable the multiple connection function).

After the multiple connection function is enabled, the TNC is initially tuned to stream A. To select a different stream, at the command prompt, type:

cmd: |*x* <CR>

where | is the default value for the *streamswitch* character and *x* is a letter (A through J) representing the desired stream. For example, to select stream B, type:

cmd: |B <CR>

After you switch streams, the terminal displays:

|Bcmd:

indicating that the TNC is now tuned to stream B. From that point on, any commands sent to the TNC are addressed to stream B until a new stream is selected. Note that the stream indication (|B) only appears after a stream switch occurs. When the command prompt is displayed again, there is no stream indication; after displaying the stream indication once, the TNC assumes that you know which stream you are addressing.

If there is activity on another stream, the stream indication will appear again, followed by the activity that has occurred on that stream. For example, if your TNC is connected to two stations, one on stream A and another on stream B and the station on stream A disconnects while you are in the converse mode on stream B, the terminal displays:

|A * DISCONNECTED**

Or if the station on stream A sends you a message, the terminal displays:

|A Who are you talking to on the other channel?

In either case, your terminal is still addressing stream B and anything you type is directed to that stream. To answer the question received on stream A, you enter the streamswitch character, the letter representing the stream to which you wish to switch, and the text of your message, as follows:

|A I am connected to the bulletin board <CR>

You may enter this without a command prompt, that is, you can switch streams directly from the converse mode (without returning to the command mode).

Sorting Out Multiple Connections

Trying to communicate on more than one stream can get a little confusing. The TNC provides some information to help you sort things out. To obtain the big picture of what is going on, use the *Cstatus* command, at the command prompt, by typing:

cmd: CStatus <CR>

The terminal will display:

A stream -Link state is: CONNECTED to *STNA* VIA *NODE1*

B stream -IO Link state is: CONNECT in progress

C stream -Link state is: DISCONNECTED

D stream -Link state is: DISCONNECTED

E stream -Link state is: DISCONNECTED

F stream -Link state is: DISCONNECTED

G stream -Link state is: DISCONNECTED

H stream -Link state is: DISCONNECTED

I stream -Link state is: DISCONNECTED

J stream -Link state is: DISCONNECTED

This display indicates the status of each stream. In this example, stream A is connected to station whose call sign is *STNA* through node/digipeater whose call sign or alias is *NODE1*, stream B is currently attempting to establish a connection, and streams C through J are disconnected. The *IO* designation indicates that input and output to and from the TNC is currently assigned to stream B, that is, anything sent between the TNC and the terminal is addressed to or received from stream B.

The TNC provides another way to sort out streams by inserting the call sign of the connected station after each display of the stream indicator. In the example above, the station on stream A sent you a message that was displayed as:

|AWho are you talking to on the other channel?

If the stream call sign indication function was enabled, that same message would have been displayed as:

|A:WA1LOU:Who are you talking to on the other channel?

Now, when something occurs on another stream, you not only know the stream where that activity is occurring, but you also are reminded of the station that is connected to that stream. By default, the stream call sign indication function is disabled. This may be changed, at the command prompt, by typing:

cmd: STREAMCa *x* <CR>

where *x* is ON to enable the stream call sign indication function or OFF to disable the function.

Multiple connection communications will keep you hopping. It takes a little getting used to, but once you get the hang of it, it's fun!

GOOD OPERATING PROCEDURES

When you start using a new mode of amateur communications, it is important to learn good operating procedures. Let's look at some of the rules of the road for good packet radio operating.

Activity Frequencies

Packet radio operation, like RTTY, SSTV, CW and other modes, uses certain portions of the Amateur Radio bands. This helps prevent interference between different modes of communications. Imagine the cacophony of CW, RTTY, SSTV and voice communications all occurring within a few kilohertz of each other! The gentlemen's agreement also provides a common meeting place for each communications mode. The operators of each mode do not have to search from one end of an amateur band to the other end to find activity in their chosen mode; the operators of their mode can be found within a known set of frequencies.

Packet radio operations are found within certain defined frequencies; it is considered good operating practice to operate within those frequencies. The accompanying sidebar delineates the specific packet radio frequencies for VHF and UHF packet radio communications. A sidebar in the HF communications chapter lists the recommended frequencies for HF packet. Indiscriminately choosing any frequency within the Amateur Radio bands to operate packet radio is no way to make friends and a good way to make enemies. Stick with the band plans and it will be easier for everyone.

Avoiding Collisions

Whenever any Amateur Radio contact is established on a frequency where there is other activity, it is good operating practice to move the contact to another frequency where there is no activity in order to avoid interference with other stations on the active frequency.

Packet radio permits more than one contact to be conducted on the same frequency because, if there is a *collision* between the transmitted packets of two or more stations, the interference is invisible to the receiving stations and each transmitting station keeps sending a packet until the receiving station is able to receive the packet perfectly. Unfortunately, as the number of transmitting stations on the same frequency increases, the number of packet collisions increases, and the number of repeated packet transmissions increases. As a result, the time it takes to transfer information between the various stations on a frequency increases and all the connections slow down to a crawl.

This means that although multiple contacts on the same frequency are possible in packet radio, it is still good operating practice to move a contact to another frequency where there is less activity especially if the frequency of the initial contact is populated by PBBSs. With fewer stations on a frequency, there will be fewer packet collisions, fewer repeated transmissions, and communications will move faster.

CQ

Calling CQ is the traditional way of attracting another Amateur Radio station for communications, and this tradition is supported in packet radio. A packet radio CQ is easily accomplished by sending some properly configured unconnected packets in the converse mode. By default, unconnected packets are CQ packets. To be sure that this is the case, at the command prompt, type:

cmd: Unproto <CR>

and if unconnected packets are configured as CQ packets, the terminal displays:

UNPROTO CQ

If CQ is not displayed, at the command prompt, type:

cmd: Unproto CQ <CR>

After configuring unconnected packets for CQ, transfer to the converse mode and enter a carriage return. Each carriage return causes the TNC to transmit an unconnected CQ packet. Your CQ packets can be received by other stations who can hear your signal without using a node or digipeater. If someone is interested in communicating with you, they can respond to your CQ by initiating a connection.

Like any other packet, an unconnected packet can collide with other packets, so do not send too many CQ packets on a congested frequency. If there is a lot of activity on frequency, it may be easier to establish a connection with a station on your Mheard list than by trying to elicit a response to a random CQ. If there is not much activity on frequency, however, a few random CQs may prove successful. Don't over do it. Anyone who can hear your station will receive one of your first few CQ packets, so dozens of CQs are unnecessary.

Beacons: The TNC Public Announcement Function

Each TNC has a beacon function which permits a station to automatically send unconnected packets at regular intervals. The purpose of the beacon function is to announce that your packet radio station is on the air. This function was included in the very early TNCs because there was very little packet radio activity at that time. Back then, new packet radio operators needed a way to let other packet radio operators know they were on the air. Without the beacon function, some of the early packet radio stations might never have found anybody to exchange packets.

Suggested Frequencies for VHF and UHF Packet Radio Activity

The following frequencies are recommended for packet radio operation by the ARRL Board of Directors, subject to local frequency coordinator recommendations. Specific use of these frequencies should be determined by local user groups. Additional frequencies (including any duplex operation) should be coordinated with local frequency coordinators.

50.62 MHz : packet radio calling channel-simplex
50.62 / 51.62 : locally coordinated duplex pair (high in, low out)
50.64 / 51.64 : locally coordinated duplex pair (high in, low out)
50.66 / 51.66 : locally coordinated duplex pair (high in, low out)
50.68 / 51.68 : locally coordinated duplex pair (high in, low out)
50.72 / 51.72 : locally coordinated duplex pair (high in, low out)
50.74 / 51.74 : locally coordinated duplex pair (high in, low out)
50.76 / 51.76 : locally coordinated duplex pair (high in, low out)
50.78 / 51.78 : locally coordinated duplex pair (high in, low out)

145.010 MHz: automatic/unattended operation (inter-LAN use)
145.030 : automatic/unattended operation
145.050 : automatic/unattended operation
145.070 : automatic/unattended operation
145.090 : automatic/unattended operation

223.42 MHz : locally coordinated packet radio simplex channel
223.44 : locally coordinated packet radio simplex channel
223.46 : locally coordinated packet radio simplex channel
223.48 : locally coordinated packet radio simplex channel
223.52 : locally coordinated packet radio channel
223.54 : locally coordinated packet radio simplex channel
223.56 : locally coordinated packet radio simplex channel
223.60 : locally coordinated packet radio simplex channel
223.62 : locally coordinated packet radio simplex channel
223.64 : locally coordinated packet radio simplex channel

430.05 MHz : 100 kHz-wide channel
430.15 : 100 kHz-wide channel
430.25 : 100 kHz-wide channel
430.35 : 100 kHz-wide channel

Times have changed. Today, there are thousands of packet radio stations on the air. Most of these stations operate on a few select frequencies within the Amateur Radio spectrum. As a result, it is not very difficult to find another station to contact. By simply using the Mheard command, you can obtain a list of recently monitored stations. It is very likely that more than one of the listed stations is still on the air and can be connected to your station. Even the newest TNCs still include the beacon function, however, and since it is there, it is still being used on the busiest packet radio frequencies in the world.

The beacon function still serves a legitimate purpose on frequencies (or in localities) where there is little packet radio activity. If you are operating a 902-MHz PBBS in Barrow, Alaska, by all means, enable the beacon function on a five-minute interval basis. If you leave your TNC on 24 hours a day on 145.01 MHz in Chevy Chase, Maryland, however, do not beacon the fact that your station is on the air. Sending beacons in such packet radio congested areas is poor operating practice. It interferes with stations trying to exchange packets on frequency and does not win many friends. Disable the beacon function and leave a message on the local PBBS that your station is on the air. Where

430.45 : 100 kHz-wide channel
430.55 : 100 kHz-wide channel
430.65 : 100 kHz-wide channel
430.85 : 100 kHz-wide channel
430.95 : 100 kHz-wide channel
431.025 : 25 kHz-wide channel
440.975 : 25 kHz-wide channel
441.000 : 25 kHz-wide channel
441.025 : 25 kHz-wide channel
441.050 :25 kHz-wide channel
441.075 :25 kHz-wide channel

903-906 MHz: packet radio-shared with other digital modes
915-918 : packet radio-shared with other digital modes

1249.0 MHz : 2 MHz-wide channel
1251.0 : 2 MHz-wide channel
1294.025: 25 kHz-wide channel
1294.050: 25 kHz-wide channel
1294.075: 25 kHz-wide channel
1294.100: 25 kHz-wide channel; National packet radio calling frequency
1294.125: 25 kHz-wide channel
1294.150: 25 kHz-wide channel
1294.175: 25 kHz-wide channel
1298.0 : 2 MHz-wide channel
1299.05 : 100 kHz-wide channel
1299.15 : 100 kHz-wide channel
1299.25 : 100 kHz-wide channel
1299.35 : 100 kHz-wide channel
1299.45 : 100 kHz-wide channel
1299.55 : 100 kHz-wide channel
1299.65 : 100 kHz-wide channel
1299.75 : 100 kHz-wide channel
1299.85 : 100 kHz-wide channel
1299.95 : 100 kHz-wide channel

2303.0-2303.5 MHz: packet radio
2303.8-2303.9 MHz: packet radio
2304.2-2304.3 : packet radio-shared with other modes
2304.4-2304.5 : packet radio-shared with other modes
2399-2399.5: packet radio

there is a fair amount of packet radio activity, anything that can be announced with a beacon is better off being announced with a message on the local PBBS.

Again, beacons still serve a legitimate purpose on certain frequencies and/or in certain localities, so a short primer on the beacon function is in order.

The contents of the beacon, (the beacon message or announcement) are stored in the TNC by means of the *Btext* command. This message can contain a maximum of 120 characters. Btext is entered, at the command prompt, by typing:

cmd: BText *x* <CR>

where *x* is the contents of the beacon message.

The beacon function may be enabled in one of two ways. It may be enabled to transmit at regular specified intervals or it may be enabled to transmit after a specified interval of packet radio inactivity. The *beacon after mode* is preferred because transmissions only occur when the channel is clear and has not been in use for some time. In the beacon after mode, the beacon is transmitted once after the set amount of time passes with no channel activity. The TNC will not send the beacon again until it detects activity on the channel and then, only after the activity has again ceased for the set interval. In the regular interval mode, beacons are transmitted at regular intervals, even during the busiest periods.

To enable the inactivity beacon mode, at the command prompt, type:

cmd: Beacon After *n* <CR>

where *n* is a number from 0 to 250 representing intervals of packet radio inactivity in 10-second increments. [For example, to select a beacon interval of 10 minutes (600 seconds), set n to 60 (600 sec / 10 sec = 60).] If n is 0, the beacon function is disabled.

To enable the regular interval beacon mode, at the command prompt, type:

cmd: Beacon Every *n* <CR>

where *n* is a number from 0 to 250 representing the interval between beacon transmissions in 10-second increments. Again, if n is 0, the beacon function is disabled.

CONCLUSION

This chapter spells out the basic operating procedures for amateur packet radio. The following chapters take these basic operating procedures and fine tune them for the various types of packet radio communications now occurring on the air: networks, HF, bulletin boards, DX packet clusters, gateways, APRS, outer space and other applications.

7

Networking

A packet radio network is a system of interconnected packet radio stations designed for the efficient transfer of packets over long distances.

In this definition, a "long distance" is any distance that is unable to support communications between two (or more) packet radio stations that wish to intercommunicate. On HF, that long distance may be across a continent. On VHF, long distance may be across a state. On UHF, long distance may be across a metropolitan area. In any case, when that "long distance" exists, packet radio stations trying to communicate over it require a network to achieve their goal.

The history of packet radio networking parallels the growth of amateur packet radio. When there were only a few amateurs using packet, packet radio networking was rudimentary, where it existed at all. But, as the packet population grew, the need for better ways of transporting packets grew, too.

Starting with no networks or rudimentary networks in the form of packet radio repeaters, the first advance in packet networking was new TNC firmware that allowed each TNC to act as a "digital repeater" (*digipeater* or *digi* for short).

Digipeaters served packet radio users well for a few years, but the burgeoning packet population demanded something better. That came in the form of NET/ROM, which was new firmware for a TNC that replaced the TNC functions with networking tools that were more intelligent than the simple digipeater.

NET/ROM also served packet radio users well for a number of years and, in one form or another, still performs the yeoman's share of packet networking today. However, hams are never satisfied. They are always tinkering to improve what already exists. As a result, a number of new packet networks were developed and vie for the attention of the packet radio net worker today.

THE IDEAL AND THE IDEAS

Say I want to send some packets to Joe Ham. First, I have to find Joe. Is he on 2 meters, 222 or 450 MHz? If he is on 2 meters, is he on 145.01, 03, 05, 07, 09 or 144.91, 93, 95, 97, 99 MHz or elsewhere? Once I find where Joe is, I have to figure out how to contact him on that frequency. Do I try a direct connection? Do I have to use a digipeater or a network node? If I need a digipeater or node, I need to know their call signs as well as Joe's. There's a lot of preliminary work involved before I can actually start talking with Joe. Once the preliminary work is done and communications are set up with Joe, I may wonder if it was all worth it because those communications can get awfully slow if there is a lot of competing communications on the same channel and/or network.

In an ideal packet world, all I would have to know is Joe's call sign. Tell the local network that I want to talk with Joe and, voila! I could start communicating with him almost immediately with little or no delay in the exchange of our data.

This ideal situation is what the packet radio net workers are trying to achieve. Each one of them is chipping away at the problem and their work has resulted in some success in achieving the ideal networking situation. The following briefly describes each of the packet radio networks in detail.

AT FIRST, THERE WERE NONE

In the beginning, there were no networks. The firmware stuffed inside the first TNCs provided no means of networking. Primordial packet radio stations could only communicate with other packet radio stations that were within earshot. To make matters worse, the lands were sparsely populated with TNCs back then. As a result, there weren't too many TNCs within earshot of each other and there wasn't too much packet radio communications. You were very lucky if you could connect with one or two other stations.

Something had to be done, otherwise packet radio would die on the vine. Taking a cue from their brethren on FM voice, the pioneering packet users began using repeaters to expand their communication horizons. With repeaters, your neighborhood grew. Instead of communicating only with your next-door neighbors, you could now communicate with neighbors who were not within earshot. As long as you and they were within earshot of the same repeater, you could connect.

Packet radio repeaters came in a variety of flavors. For example, packet users in Washington, DC, used a standard 2-meter voice repeater. In San Francisco, a simplex repeater served the Bay Area packet users. In Montreal, a store-and-forward repeater expanded the local network.

DIGIPEATERS: A REPEATER IN EVERY TNC

Repeaters, whatever their flavor, made a big difference in the capabilities of the packet radio network. To take advantage of the potential that repeaters offered, the writers of the AX.25 packet radio protocol included digital repeater capabilities in that protocol. Now, any TNC that was compatible with AX.25 had the digipeater capability built into its firmware. A user only had to issue a command to a TNC and the TNC could repeat packets.

The TNC's digipeater function is controlled by the means of the "Digipeat" command and, by default, is enabled. In the spirit of cooperation among packet radio stations, nearly every packet radio operator leaves the digipeater capability enabled. If you need to change the status of this function for some reason, at the command prompt, type:

cmd: DIGIpeat *x* <CR>

where *x* is ON to enable or OFF to disable the digipeater function.

If point-to-point communications are possible without using a digipeater, then don't use a digipeater. In fact, it's best to use an unoccupied frequency when possible. Packets are transferred between stations more quickly when the stations are communicating directly with each other; at the same time, the digipeater is freed up to serve stations that cannot communicate point-to-point. This is analogous to using FM voice simplex operation rather than a voice repeater whenever possible.

If point-to-point communications are not possible, then go ahead and use a digipeater. To use a digipeater, a user only has to add "Via" and the call sign of the digipeater when invoking the Connect command. For example, to connect with a station by means of a digipeater, the user enters the following at the command prompt:

cmd: Connect *W1AW* Via *DIGI* <CR>

where *W1AW* is the call sign of the station to be connected with and *DIGI* is the call sign of the digipeater.

The big drawback of the original digi-in-a-TNC function was that a user could only exploit one digipeater to make a connection. If the station you wanted to connect with was more than one digipeater hop away, you were out of luck. The AX.25 writers addressed this problem when they revised the protocol. The new version of AX.25 permits users to address as many as eight digipeaters to make a connection. The user again has to add Via to the Connect command, but now may add as many as eight digipeater call signs (separated by commas) after Via. For example:

cmd: Connect *W1AW* Via *DIGI-1, DIGI-2, DIGI-3,...* DIGI-8 <CR>

where *W1AW* is the call sign of the station to be connected with and *DIGI-1, -2, -3* through *-8* are the call signs of the digipeaters.

Note that commas (,) separate the digipeater station call signs and that SSIDs must be included if the station's SSID is anything other than 0. Also, note that the order of digipeater call signs is critical. The first digipeater call sign must be the digipeater station that is the first to receive and transmit your transmissions, while the last digipeater call sign is the last to receive and repeat your transmissions. Another way to put it is the first digipeater call sign is the digipeater closest to your station, while the last digipeater call sign is the digipeater closest to the station that you are trying to contact.

There are two types of digipeaters. The most often used digipeaters are those that are dedicated to digipeater operation. These dedicated digipeaters are similar to voice repeaters in that they serve no other function except to act as a repeater. Like voice repeaters, they are often located in high places to provide the best coverage for the area they serve. Also, like voice repeaters, many dedicated digipeaters are listed in *The ARRL Repeater Directory*. Check the directory for the digipeater nearest you.

The second type of digipeater is a station that normally serves as someone's personal packet radio station. Such a station is used by its owner to contact other packet stations and is not a dedicated digipeater. As we mentioned earlier, however, any [illegible] able of acting as a digipeater; if someone's home station is located in a [illegible] n yours, you may occasionally call upon the better-located station [illegible] r.

[illegible] of digipeaters are nearly identical. They both use the same equipment [illegible] ansceiver and an antenna) and you use the same TNC command to [illegible] of either type of digipeater. The only difference is that a dedicated digipeate[illegible] ays available to serve you (barring power outages or equipment malfunctions), whereas the home packet radio station is not always available for your use. The owner may be operating on a different frequency or in a different mode, or the station may be off the air.

The packet radio network of digipeaters was very successful. Packet users could digipeat to TNCs in far off states and provinces. The network worked so well that packet bulletin board systems (PBBSs), which originally were set up for the interchange of mail between local users, could now use the network to exchange mail with users of remote PBBSs.

NET/ROM: A NETWORK NODE IN A TNC

Packet users parked packet radio stations on mountain tops and high manmade structures to serve as dedicated digipeaters. The network grew quickly and became so complex that packet users compiled and distributed digipeater maps to inform users as to how to find a path between here and there.

The problem was that the network was so dynamic; changes could occur at any time. Turning off an old TNC or turning on a new one could change the complexion of the network instantly. New paths appeared and old paths disappeared unpredictably. As a result, digipeater maps were out-of-date almost as soon as they were finished. Users did not know which mapped paths still existed, nor which paths were the best paths.

The solution to the problem was NET/ROM. The brain child of Ron Raikes, WA8DED, and Mike Busch, W6IXU, NET/ROM consisted of firmware on an EPROM that replaced one of the EPROMs in a TNC.

Like the network, NET/ROM is dynamic. It continually updates its path information. It knows when a new path is available and it knows when an old path is broken. So, it always is aware of the best path that is available at any time. Also, NET/ROM is not limited to the eight hops of digipeating. It can use as many nodes as necessary to make a connection. Another advantage of NET/ROM is that its throughput is better than that of digipeaters because it uses *node-to-node acknowledgment* rather than the digipeater-style *end-to-end acknowledgment*.

As its popularity grew, NET/ROM begot other networking schemes that were similar to NET/ROM, like TheNet and KA-Node, and networking schemes that were completely different like TexNet, ROSE and TCP/IP. These networks now inhabit every nook and cranny of the packet radio world.

How NET/ROM Works

The NET/ROM network user no longer has to be concerned with the digipeater path required to get from one point to another. All the user needs to know is the local node of the station he wishes to contact. NET/ROM knows what path is required and if one path is not working or breaks down for some reason, NET/ROM will switch to an alternative path, if one exists.

The user can be assured that NET/ROM is on top of things because each NET/ROM node automatically updates its node list periodically and, whenever a new node comes on the air, the other NET/ROM nodes become aware of the new node's existence automatically. In addition to automatic route updating, routing information may also be updated manually by means of a terminal keyboard or remotely using a packet radio connection.

Once you are connected to another station via the NET/ROM network, most of your packets get through because node-to-node packet acknowledgment is used rather than end-to-end acknowledgment. When a user sends a packet from one point to another via the AX.25 digipeater network, his packet is simply handed off from one digipeater to another. If the intended destination station receives the packet without error, it sends an acknowledgment back along the same hand-to-hand path. Anywhere along the path, the packet or acknowledgment may collide with another packet and be lost. If the packet is lost, the originating station does not receive an acknowledgment of receipt from the destination station, so it sends the packet along the entire path again.

When a user sends a packet through a NET/ROM network, things are done differently. Each time the packet is transferred to a new node, that new node sends an acknowledgment of receipt back to the previous node. If a packet or acknowledgment is lost, only the unacknowledged node has to resend the packet (to the next node). The originating station does not have to send the packet through the entire path.

Besides offering node-to-node acknowledgment, NET/ROM also allows you to build cross-frequency or cross-band multiport nodes. This is done by installing NET/ROM in two TNCs and connecting their serial ports together. In addition to providing these sophisticated functions, NET/ROM also provides the standard AX.25 digipeater function.

NET/ROM uses AX.25 for links between neighboring nodes and links with its local users. In addition, NET/ROM uses a transport layer sliding window protocol that provides end-to-end error control to counteract lost, duplicate or out-of-sequence packet frames that result from node failures and path changes. The *sliding window protocol* also provides end-to-end flow control to assure that one particular path is not disproportionately loaded with traffic. Since NET/ROM strictly separates the Network and Transport layers and provides a datagram-network service at *Level 3*, it is possible that NET/ROM can be used as a subnetwork for TCP/IP and other higher-level network systems.

How to Use a Node

Using a NET/ROM or TheNet node is simple. Before we look at how to use a network node, it should be stated that most nodes use a mnemonic identifier instead of their FCC-given call signs. Typically, the identifier is a three-to-six character acronym that identifies the node's location. The reason for using identifiers is to simplify what the user has to remember. For example, instead of having to remember that XK1NG is the network node located in Kong Island, all you have to remember is the node's mnemonic identifier, KONG.

To use a network node, you first connect to your local node by entering the Connect command at the command prompt as follows:

cmd: CONNECT *URNODE* <CR>

where *URNODE* is the call sign or mnemonic identifier of the local node.

After you connect to your local node, you may connect to another station that is also local to your node or you may connect to a distant node. To connect to another station, enter the Connect command as follows:

Connect *OTHRSTN* <CR>

where *OTHRSTN* is the call sign of that other station.

To connect to a distant node, enter the Connect command prompt as follows:

Connect *DXNODE* <CR>

where *DXNODE* is the call sign or mnemonic identifier of the distant node.

After the local node establishes a connection with the distant node, use the "Connect *OTHRSTN*" command to connect to a station that is local to the other node.

Note that the commands used to connect your TNC to a node and to ask a node to connect to another node or station are different. When you connect your TNC to a node, you are using the TNC's Connect command. When you ask a node to connect to another node or station, you are using the node's Connect command. To assure that a node receives a node command (and not be misinterpreted by your TNC as a TNC command), do not send a node command until you connect to a node, that is, after you receive the node connection message. If you send the node command too soon, the TNC will try to interpret it and, when it can't, send you an error message.

Also note that when the distant node makes a connection with the distant station, it uses your call sign with an SSID different from that of your TNC. The SSID used by the network node is determined by subtracting your SSID from 15; for example, a distant node will change WA1LOU-0 to WA1LOU-15 (15 – 0 = 15).

Finally note that network nodes have inactivity timers that will summarily disconnect you if you have not sent anything to the node within the time set in the inactivity timer (the default setting is 15 minutes).

How you disconnect depends on how you are using the network node. Many network nodes support the "Bye" command, so simply invoking the Bye command will disconnect you from the network node. If the network node does not support the Bye command, then you must first switch your TNC to the command mode (via <CTRL-C>) and then invoke the Disconnect command. The Disconnect command will disconnect you from all the nodes you are using as well as any the distant stations you happen to be connected to, thus, saving you the trouble of disconnecting from each node and station yourself.

If you are not connected to a distant station, but are connected to one or more nodes, network nodes will respond to other commands besides Connect. A summary of the other commands that network nodes will recognize appears in the accompanying sidebar titled "Network Node User Commands."

Network Node User Commands

NET/ROM

A description of each NET/ROM user command follows. All, except CQ, may be invoked by using the first letter of the command. Entering anything other than a NET/ROM command will cause the node to list the commands. Note that these commands are used only after you have connected with a NET/ROM node (using your TNC's "Connect" command).

Connect *x* – Causes a node to initiate a connection with another node or user whose call sign or node identifier is *x*.

CQ *x* – Causes a node to send "CQ" followed by text whose contents is *x*.

Nodes – Causes a node to send you a list of nodes that are connectable from the local node.

Routes – Causes a node to send you its information about other nodes.

Users – Causes a node to send you a list of stations that are using the node.

TheNet

A description of each TheNet user command follows. Entering anything other than a TheNet command will cause the node to list the commands. Note that these commands are used only after you have connected with a TheNet node (using your TNC's "Connect" command).

ARP – Causes a node to send you its TCP/IP ARP route table.

BBS – Causes a node to connect you to a local BBS.

Bye – Disconnects you from a node.

Connect *x* – Causes a node to initiate a connection with another node or user whose call sign or node identifier is *x*.

CQ *x* – Causes a node to send "CQ" followed by text whose contents is *x*.

DXcluster – Causes a node to connect you to a local DXcluster.

Host – Causes a node to connect you to a local host, which is typically a local BBS.

Help – Causes a node to send you information about its user commands.

Info – Causes a node to send you information about the node.

IProute – Causes a node to send you its TCP/IP IP route table.

MHeard – Causes a node to send you a list of stations and information concerning those stations that the node has recently heard.

Nodes – Causes a node to send you a list of nodes that are connectable from the local node.

Quit – Disconnects you from a node.

Routes – Causes a node to send you its information about other nodes.

Stats – Causes a node to send you statistical data concerning the node.

Talk – Allows stations to hold a roundtable conference. When in the Talk mode, anything sent by a station is copied to all other stations in the conference.

Users – Causes a node to send you a list of stations that are using the node.

KA-NODE

KA-Node is the Kantronics implementation of a node-to-node acknowledgment protocol. Except for the original KPC-1, the KA-Node function is available in every Kantronics TNC and in the Kantronics All Mode (KAM) controllers. As explained in the description of NET/ROM above, node-to-node acknowledgment provides improved throughput over the standard AX.25 end-to-end acknowledgment. Besides node-to-node acknowledgment, KA-Node allows you to gateway from one port to another when you are connected to a dual-port KA-Node, which is available in the Kantronics KAM, KAM Plus and KPC-4.

Whereas KA-Node and NET/ROM are similar in that they both offer node-to-node acknowledgment, they are dissimilar in other ways. The most important difference is that KA-Node does not perform automatic routing as does NET/ROM. Instead, the user must command the KA-Node as to the desired path to another node or station. In this way, KA-Node is more like an AX.25 digipeater than a NET/ROM node. Although KA-Node does not achieve the same functionality of NET/ROM, it is still an improvement over digipeating and, as a result, it is a popular packet radio tool.

How To Use KA-Node

From the user's perspective, using a KA-Node is similar to using a NET/ROM node. The first thing you do is make a connection to your local KA-Node by typing (at the command prompt):

cmd: Connect *NODE-A* <CR>

where *NODE-A* is the KA-Node identifier of the KA-Node. Your terminal will display a message indicating that you are now connected to a KA-Node and it is awaiting your command. To make a connection to another station that is in the operating range of the KA-Node, you type:

Connect *OTHRSTN* <CR>

where *OTHRSTN* is the call sign of the other station. To make a connection to another KA-Node that is in the operating range of the KA-Node A, you type:

Connect *NODE-B* <CR>

where *NODE-B* is the KA-Node identifier of the other KA-Node. In either case, KA-Node A will attempt to establish a connection and, if it is successful, your terminal displays:

####LINK MADE

If the connection has been made to another station, you may now communicate with the other station.

If the connection has been made to another KA-Node, your terminal will also display a message indicating that you are now connected to another KA-Node and it is awaiting your command.

If you wish, you can make a connection to yet another KA-Node (KA-Node C) that is in the operating range of KA-Node B. Here is where the difference between a KA-Node and NET/ROM-type node is conspicuous. If you were using NET/ROM-type nodes in this example rather than KA-Nodes, the NET/ROM node may have been able to make the connection between Nodes A and C automatically, that is, you may have been able to command Node A to connect with Node C and have avoided manually making the intermediary connection to Node B. (Node A may in fact use Node B as an intermediary to connect to Node C, but that would be transparent to the user.) The automatic routing feature of NET/ROM makes this possible.

Without automatic routing, the KA-Node user must do the routing manually, however, KA-Node does provide some assistance in this regard. By invoking the "Nodes" command, KA-Node will provide you with a list of both KA-Node and NET/ROM nodes that the local KA-Node has heard along with the date and times of such monitoring. The Nodes command is similar to the "MHeard" command in your TNC and may be used in a similar way. Just as you use the MHeard command to inform you as to what stations are connectable from your station, you can use the Nodes command to inform you what nodes are connectable from the local KA-Node.

KA-Node also allows the user to obtain a list of everything that it has heard (individual stations, PBBSs, digipeaters, as well as, nodes) by invoking the "Jheard" command. In effect, the Jheard command causes the KA-Node to dump its MHeard log to you. This can be useful if you need to know if another station in range of the local KA-Node has been recently active or to find out what PBBSs and digipeaters are connectable from the local KA-Node. (All of the KA-Node user commands are listed and described in the accompanying sidebar titled "KA-Node User Commands.")

ROSE: THE X.25 PACKET NETWORK

The Radio Amateur Telecommunications Society's many packet radio efforts fall

KA-Node User Commands

A description of each KA-Node user command follows. Note that these commands are used only after you have connected with a KA-Node node (using your TNC's "Connect" command).

Abort – Causes a node to stop acting on your Connect or XConnect request.

Bye – Disconnects you from a node.

Connect *x* – Causes a node to initiate a connection with another node or user whose call sign or node identifier is *x*.

Help – Causes a node to list and briefly describe its command set.

JHeard – Causes a node to send you a list of stations and information concerning those stations that the node has recently heard.

JHeard S – Causes a node to send you a list of stations that the node has recently heard without the date and time of monitoring.

JHeard L – Causes a node to send you a list of stations that the node has recently heard along with the destination stations worked and the digipeaters used, if any.

Nodes – Causes a node to send you a list of other KA-Nodes and NET/ROM nodes it has heard recently along with the date and time of monitoring.

XConnect *x* – Causes a node to initiate a connection on its other port with another node or user whose call sign or node identifier is *x*.

under the umbrella of the "RATS" Open Systems Environment (ROSE). ROSE includes a packet radio bulletin board (*ROSErver/PRMBS*, the *Packet Radio MailBox System*), an on-line call sign directory and database server with graphical capabilities (*ROSErver/OCS*), a multicast protocol (ROSE/BBC), ROSE/STS Station Traffic System, as well as the ROSE X.25 Packet Switch. The ROSE switch is the basic element of ROSE X.25 Packet Networks.

Much of the world's communications is done using computers. Telecommunications professionals have developed many methods for computer networking. One of the standard methods is X.25. When radio amateurs in the U.S. began work on a way for "hams" to enter the age of computer communications, X.25 was chosen as the foundation upon which to build.

The RATS implementation of X.25 is the ROSE X.25 Packet Switch. Networks made up of ROSE switches provide amateurs with a vehicle through which they can easily establish packet connections with other stations. Connections through a ROSE network can be thought of as a "reliable data pipe."

Using ROSE X.25 Packet Networks is similar to using the telephone network. Phones are easy to use. All one has to do is find a phone (the entry point into the network), dial the desired telephone number (the "network address" of the exit point from the network) and ask, by name, for the desired party (the person's "User ID").

How the call is processed by the telephone network is irrelevant; all that matters is that the call goes through. A call from New York to California may go through Chicago, St. Louis or Atlanta, but all that matters to the caller is that it goes through automatically and reliably. (The telephone network did not always work this way. At one time, an operator in one city had to call the operator in the next city and so on, to get a call through to the desired party. But, even then, the caller did not choose the call's route.)

With ROSE networks, users must know their entry point into the network (their local ROSE switch), the exit point to reach the desired station (the ROSE address of the switch used by that station) and the call sign of the desired station ("User ID"). Like the telephone network, the ROSE network determines the path taken by the call.

ROSE addresses follow the international standards used by commercial X.25 data networks. These addresses are based upon the telephone numbering plan used in each country. In North America, this is the telephone Area Code and Exchange. Area Codes and Exchanges are assigned geographically and, as a result, ROSE addresses indicate a geographical area, too.

The building block of ROSE X.25 Packet Networks is the ROSE X.25 Packet Switch. The ROSE switch is implemented as an EPROM replacement for most available TNCs. It is free for noncommercial Amateur Radio use.

How to Use ROSE Networks

ROSE networks are easy to use, as you will see in the following example.

In the ROSE network, there is the KB2ICI-7 *ROSErver/OCS Online Callbook Server* at ROSE address 609426 (central New Jersey) and there is a ROSE switch in New York City, KB7UV-3. A user of the KB7UV-3 ROSE switch can connect to the *Online Callbook Server* by sending the TNC the following command:

cmd: Connect KB2ICI-7 Via KB7UV-3,609426 <CR>

The call sign of the entry ROSE switch (KB7UV-3) is placed in the first digipeater field and the desired ROSE address (609426) is placed in the second digipeater field.

The user's terminal will first display the "connected to" message from the TNC followed by a network message that acknowledges the call request, as follows:

***** CONNECTED to KB2ICI-7 VIA KB7UV-3,609426**

Call being Setup

Once the connection has been established, an additional message will be sent by the network :

Call Complete to KB2ICI-7@3100609426

This message includes the call sign of the station connected to (KB2ICI-7) and the complete ROSE address of the switch which made the final link (3100609426). This "complete" address includes country identification information. In this example, "3100" is the Amateur Radio Data Network Identification Code (DNIC) for the U.S.

At this point, there is a connection between the two stations through the network. Either station can end the connection by simply issuing a Disconnect command to their TNC. The network will advise the other station of this by sending the message:

***** Call Clearing**

***** 0000 3100609426 Remote Station cleared connection**

ROSE X.25 networks also inform users of other situations through similar messages (other station busy, etc.). Each message, as indicated above, includes a ROSE address (3100609426) to indicate the point in the network where the condition described in the message has occurred.

Unlike some other approaches to packet networking, the call signs of stations using ROSE networks are never modified in any way and the call sign of the station transmitting a given packet frame is never in question. All transmissions by ROSE X.25 packet switches indicate the call sign of the transmitting station using the "last repeated" bit. When monitoring with most TNCs, this is indicated by an asterisk (*) next to the call sign.

On-line Help and Directories

Help is always available to users of ROSE networks. Each ROSE switch has informative text stored in memory. To obtain this text, you connect directly to the switch and send a carriage return or wait 30 seconds. The text, which usually includes information on the network and basic instructions on switch operation, will be sent to you.

ROSE networks can also have directories of services (PBBSs, ROSE switches, etc) and other information available to users, if implemented by the network managers. This is done through the *ROSE INFO* application and special ROSE addresses.

The ROSE network uses special addresses made up of Area Code and either "555" or "411" for directories. The 555 directories are for services and 411 directories are for users. If a user of the N2DSY-3 ROSE switch wants information on services available in southern New Jersey (Area Code 609), the user issues this command to a TNC:

cmd: Connect INFO Via N2DSY-3, 609555 <CR>

This is automatically routed to the switch containing the directory information. Once the call is completed, the directory text is sent to the user.

Other Services

Optionally, ROSE networks can have very useful applications. The most popular are HEARD and USERS. HEARD provides a list of stations heard by a given switch and USERS provides a list of switch activity. Both are used in the same way, that is, you initiate a connection to the desired application at the ROSE address of interest and, if the application is loaded at that switch, the requested information will be sent.

Refer to the accompanying sidebar ("RATS Open System Environment") for a summary of the parts that comprise ROSE.

TCP/IP: *NET*, *NOS* AND BEYOND

An early proposal for higher-level packet radio networking was presented by Phil Karn, KA9Q, at the Fourth ARRL Amateur Radio Computer Networking Conference in March 1985. Phil proposed that Amateur Radio adopt TCP/IP, the Defense Advanced Research Projects Agency (DARPA) *Internet Protocol* (*IP*) and *Transmission Control Protocol* (*TCP*), as the standard Level 3 (Network layer) and Level 4 (Transport layer) protocols for amateur packet radio.

Despite the name, TCP and IP are only two parts of a collection or "suite" of protocols that comprise the complete DARPA protocol, which permits different types of computers to communicate with each other. The DARPA protocols are used on hundreds of landline networks to interconnect mainframe computers in universities, government research centers (typically, Defense Department contractors) and other commercial interests throughout the world.

In 1987, Phil Karn, KA9Q, wrote the amateur packet radio implementation of TCP/IP for DOS-based computers and called it *NET*. Two years later, Phil rewrote and refined the software and called it *Network Operating System* or *NOS*, for short. Others have modified *NOS* and, today, it comes in a variety of flavors. The software has also been ported to the Macintosh, Amiga, Atari and UNIX computer systems.

The Virtues of TCP/IP

The TCP/IP software emulates many of the functions of a TNC. As a result, the computer is no longer limited to the functions programmed into the TNC's read-only memory and may be programmed to do much more including what follows.

Imagine this. You are at your computer chatting keyboard-to-keyboard with station A, while in the background, your computer is receiving a file from station B and delivering a message to station C. You don't have to imagine this scenario. Instead you can actually experience it if you use TCP/IP because it allows your computer to perform all of these functions and, what's more, perform them simultaneously!

One of the main functions of the TCP/IP software is to allow each TCP/IP station to function as an intelligent part of the network. TCP/IP stations are "intelligent" because they can automatically route packets to their intended destination without any operator intervention or direction. TCP/IP frees the operator of the task of figuring out which string of digipeaters or local and remote network nodes must be used to get packets delivered to their intended destination. The operator simply commands the software to communicate with station X and the network does the rest of the work automatically determining the proper route for getting the communications to the proper station.

RATS Open Systems Environment

Radio Amateur Telecommunications Society is in an open approach to packet development. To be part of the RATS Open Systems Environment, a project must be free for noncommercial Amateur Radio use and source code must be available to serious developers wishing to join the project. RATS requires that all developers using ROSE source code, in whole or in part as any part of their own projects, provide full source code for their work to RATS. This ensures that the open, shared approach to development continues.

The current elements of ROSE are:

ROSE X.25 Packet Switch

This is the X.25 Packet Networking solution for the TAPR TNC 2, its clones and compatibles. The ROSE Switch is based upon international standard protocols as defined by CCITT and ISO. The ROSE Switch conforms fully to FCC and most other nation's identification requirements, does not waste channel bandwidth with needless broadcasts or beacons and has low protocol overhead increasing actual data throughput. It is written by Tom Moulton, W2VY.

ROSErver/PRMBS, the Packet Radio MailBox System

ROSErver/PRMBS is a fully WØRLI-forwarding compatible PBBS with an advanced user interface including an Internet-compatible mailer. PRMBS provides the user and SYSOP with many powerful features. ROSErver/PRMBS is written by Brian Riley, KA2BQE.

ROSErver/OCS On-line Callbook Server

OCS provides either a text-based or an efficient graphic user interface depending on the terminal capabilities of the user. Developed by Keith Sproul, WU2Z, and Mark Sproul, KB2ICI, this advanced packet server operates on the Apple Macintosh.

ROSE/BBC Bulletin Broadcast Controller

BBC provides a mechanism for simultaneous reception of packet bulletins by several stations with complete data integrity and error correction. ROSE/BBC protocol was written by Gordon Beattie, N2DSY, and the software has been implemented for UNIX by Marsh Gosnell, AD2H.

ROSE/STS Station Traffic System

The ROSE/STS Station Traffic System is a complete NTS message management system, especially suited for packet, STS runs on MS-DOS and UNIX computers and is written by Frank Warren, KB4CYC.

Besides intelligent networking, the TCP/IP software has a packet radio terminal function called *Telnet* which allows you to communicate keyboard-to-keyboard with another TCP/IP station. Using Telnet, you can have a real-time conversation with the operator at another TCP/IP station or you can log onto the mailbox system of another TCP/IP station. A file transfer function called the *File Transfer Protocol* (*FTP*) allows you to send and receive (upload and download) ASCII and binary files to and from any other TCP/IP station.

The TCP/IP software includes a built-in mail function called the *Simple Mail Transfer Protocol* (*SMTP*) that automatically sends mail you create to their destination across the TCP/IP network. If your station is not on the air all the time, the *Post Office Protocol* (*POP*) stores your mail at another designated station, which automatically sends it to you when your station comes on. The *Packet Internet Groper* (*PING*) allows you to send a packet to another TCP/IP station to check if it is on the air and *FINGER* allows you to obtain a blurb about any TCP/IP station that is on the air.

Other features of the TCP/IP software include the ability to communicate with packet radio stations who are using plain vanilla AX.25 instead of TCP/IP. Dan Frank, W9NK, also wrote software that is built into the TCP/IP software that allows TCP/IP packet radio stations to act as NET/ROM nodes for the transfer of AX.25 and TCP/IP packets.

How TCP/IP Works

The TCP/IP protocol is based on the *datagram* concept. A datagram is a self-contained message that includes the complete source and destination addresses of the message, as well as control information and the actual contents of the message. Each datagram is independent of other datagrams and, as a result, each must include all of the information needed to route it through the network.

IP (Internet Protocol) is a Level 3 or Network layer protocol that keeps track of the network node addresses, while routing outgoing packets and recognizing packets that are intended for the local node. IP is assisted by the *Address Resolution Protocol* (*ARP*), which provides the datagram address format required by IP, while being aware of any manually generated routing tables that were created for the datagram routing function. (Users may specify the datagram route, just as a user specifies a digipeater route using the AX.25 Connect command.)

IP uses a 32-bit binary number to address a packet. Each network *host*, that is, each computer at each packet radio station in the TCP/IP network, has a unique *IP address* that has been assigned by the local IP address coordinator. ARPANET assigned the address block starting with the digits 44 to amateur packet radio (as well as naming the amateur TCP/IP packet radio network *AMPRNET*). As a result, the first two digits of all amateur packet radio IP addresses are 44 (for example, the IP address of WA1LOU is 44.88.4.8).

When a connect request is initiated, IP uses the IP address for the destination network node rather than a call sign. The destination node uses its call sign in response and, thereafter, the destination call sign is used for outgoing frames at AX.25 Level 2 in order to conform with FCC regulations with regard to call signs.

TCP (Transport Control Protocol) is a Level 4 or Transport layer protocol that provides data integrity between the data's points of origination and destination, whenever such integrity is required. It assembles data for transmission into packets and

TCP/IP True Facts Revealed

There are a number of misconceptions about TCP/IP that have caused some potential TCP/IP users to steer clear of it. Let me address these misconceptions.

You must keep your radio equipment and computer on 24 hours a day.

For the viability of the TCP/IP network (not to mention your local electric company), around-the-clock operation is preferable; however, it is not a necessity as far as receiving mail is concerned. If your TCP/IP station is on the air all the time, it is always ready to receive traffic heading its way. If it is not on all the time, however, other TCP/IP stations using the Post Office Protocol (POP) can intercept and hold your station's traffic for automatic delivery to your station at a time when it is on the air.

You must use a DOS-based computer.

Although the majority of computers using TCP/IP are DOS-based, versions of TCP/IP for other computers do exist. Most notable are versions for the Apple Macintosh, Commodore Amiga, Atari ST computers and systems running UNIX.

You must use a fast computer with a lot of RAM and hard disk storage.

Relatively slow computers such as IBM PCs and Macintosh Plus's are used successfully in the amateur TCP/IP world every day. Fast clocks and oodles of memory and disk storage are nice luxuries, but you can TCP/IP without them.

TCP/IP cuts you off from the rest of the packet radio world.

Most of the bulletins that are distributed through the AX.25 packet radio world also get distributed in the TCP/IP world. Moreover, TCP/IP bulletin distribution is better because instead of wading through all of the bulletins on your local BBS trying to find something of interest to read, TCP/IP automatically routes only those bulletins of interest to you to your TCP/IP mailbox. For instance, I am on the mailing list for Macintosh computer related bulletins and messages and, as a result, all Mac-related bulletins and messages that are addressed to the Macintosh mailing list are automatically delivered to my mailbox. You can be on as many mailing lists as you desire and your mailbox will runneth over.

Also, you are not necessarily cut off from AX.25 mail-forwarding as there are many AX.25-to-TCP/IP gateway stations that will forward your mail between the two networks.

disassembles received packets into received data, while checking for errors and managing packet transmissions on the network. When TCP is not required, the *User Datagram Protocol* (*UDP*) is available at Level 4 to perform other functions.

The *Serial Line Interface Protocol* (*SLIP*) is a Level 2 or Link layer protocol that provides a simple serial data transfer between the Network layer protocols and the EIA-232 interface of the Physical layer. *KISS*, for "Keep It Simple, Stupid," is a Link layer non-protocol for serial input and output that was written by Mike Chepponis, K3MC. When KISS is turned on in your TNC, AX.25 is turned off and, as a result, no AX.25 connection is established with the other end of the circuit. Instead, KISS accepts serial data from the computer and sends it as AX.25 unconnected information (UI) packet frames (the packet radio equivalent of the datagram). Received datagrams are transferred directly to the computer for disassembly by TCP. In effect, the TCP/IP software performs much of the work that, up to now, has been performed by our TNCs.

Jump-Starting TCP/IP

Assuming you already have the requisite computer and radio equipment, you need three additional things to get started: a KISSable TNC, an IP address and the TCP/IP software itself.

When I told you that the TCP/IP software emulates many of the functions of a TNC, you may have thought that it would allow you to get into packet radio without buying a TNC or that you could throw your old one away (or at least sell it). Well, you still need a TNC and it must be one that supports the KISS mode. Virtually all current TNCs support KISS and many of the older ones that don't support KISS can be made KISSable by updating the ROM containing the TNC software. (If the software programmed in your TNC's ROM is compatible with TAPR TNC 2 software release 1.1.6 or later, then it is KISSable.)

Once your TNC is KISSable, you enable the KISS mode at the command mode by typing:

cmd: KISS ON <CR>

Note that you must use a terminal or a computer running terminal emulation software to enable the KISS mode; you cannot use the TCP/IP software to enable the KISS mode. Next, toggle the TNC's power off and on. If KISS is enabled, the STA and CON front panel indicators will blink three times as the TNC is initialized.

Next you need an IP address, which is a unique number assigned to the computer used at your packet radio station for communications over the TCP/IP network. To get an IP address, contact your local IP address coordinator. If you don't know who is your local IP address coordinator, ask other TCP/IP users in your area who the coordinator is. If all else fails, contact the author of this book. I usually have the current coordinator list and will gladly look up your coordinator.

Finally, you need the software. The sidebar titled "Software Sources" tells you where you can get TCP/IP software.

After you have acquired these three items, you can begin preparations for getting on the air with TCP/IP. First, make a copy of the TCP/IP software package and put the original copy away. You will work with the copy. If you have a hard disk and prefer working from that medium rather than from a floppy disk, copy the TCP/IP software package to the hard disk.

The TCP/IP software package will include a flock of files and subdirectories.

Software Sources

NET/ROM – Contact Ron Raikes, WA8DED (9211 Pico Vista Rd., Downey, CA 90240) concerning the availability of NET/ROM.

TheNet – May be downloaded from CompuServe's HamNet (Library 9). Your local ham radio landline BBS may also have the software.

KA-Node – Contained in the firmware of Kantronics TNCs and multi-mode controllers. Kantronics' address is 1202 E. 23rd St., Lawrence, KS 66046-5006, phone 913-842-7745, fax 913-842-2031.

ROSE – Software is available by downloading it from the KB7UV ROSErver/PRMBS at 718-956-7133 (1200-9600 V.32, 8N1, don't press Enter, wait for the sign-on message) or RATS Software Server at 201-387-8898 (1200-9600 V.32, 8N1). Additionally, new releases may be downloaded from CompuServe's HamNet (Library 9). For those without access to EPROM programming equipment, RATS can "burn" ROSE Switch EPROMs at cost. Also, they will be happy to copy their software onto your disks, provided you supply return postage.

TCP/IP – Software may be downloaded from CompuServe's HamNet (library 9). It may be obtained by ftp'ing it via the Internet from the following sites: ftp.ucsd.edu or oak.oakland.edu. It is also available on disk from TAPR (8987-309 E. Tanque Verde Rd., Tucson, AZ 85749-9399, phone 817-383-0000, fax 817-566-2544). Your local ham radio landline BBS may have the software, too.

TexNet – Available from the Texas Packet Radio Society, Inc., P.O. Box 50238, Denton, TX 76206-0238.

Note that different versions of *NOS* may have different file and subdirectory requirements. Also, when I say "subdirectory," Macintosh users should think "folder."

You must modify files in the KA9Q package to contain your IP address and other information. Also, the placement of files within computer directories and subdirectories is critical (and varies with computer), so refer to the software documentation on how to modify, set up and locate the necessary files.

Setting Up the Software

Since the TCP/IP software varies between authors and computers, it is impossible to provide a complete soup to nuts menu of how to modify everything you need to get up and running. For example, Ian Wade, G3NRW, wrote a whole book (titled *NOSintro)* that explains how to set up and use just the KA9Q version of *NOS*. (The book is available from the ARRL.) So, what follows is a general guideline of what files you will have to modify. You will have to refer to your software's documentation for the specifics.

You will have to modify the *autoexec.**** and *hosts.net* or *domain.txt* files and it is also useful to modify the *alias* file and *finger* and *pub* subdirectories at this time as well. (The suffix of the file name *autoexec.**** is different depending upon the software you are using.) You can use a simple text editor to modify these files or you can use a word processor to do the job, but you must save the word processor work in plain text or ASCII format; otherwise, the files will be unusable by your TCP/IP software.

autoexec.*

Your TCP/IP software uses *autoexec.**** whenever you start running the program. It contains information that is unique to your station and, thus, configures *the software* to be compatible with your station. Some parameters in *autoexec.**** must be modified immediately, while other parameters may be changed later after you become more experienced with TCP/IP.

To get things started, you must modify the following *autoexec.**** parameters:

- ip addr [(*insert your IP address*)], for example, ip addr 044.088.004.008
- hostname (*insert your call sign*).ampr.org, for example, hostname wa1lou.ampr.org
- ax25 mycall (*insert your call sign and SSID*), for example, ax25 mycall wa1lou-0

Note that you may shorten your IP address (almost everybody does) by eliminating the first and second zero in each quadrant of the address, thus, I shortened my IP address (044.088.004.008) to 44.88.4.8. The IP address entry in my *autoexec.**** reads "ip addr [44.88.0.14]."

- tzone (*insert the initials of your Time Zone followed by a space and the number of hours your Time Zone differs with Greenwich Mean Time*), e.g., tzone EST 5

The next two items, "attach" and "route," are a little complicated. They must be set correctly or your software will not operate properly. Attach determines which computer port the TCP/IP software will use to communicate with the TNC and how. The *autoexec.**** file that is included in your computer's TCP/IP software package has the attach parameter already set for the typical configuration of your computer for TCP/IP operation. For example, in the IBM/MS-DOS version of *NOS*, the attach parameter is preset as follows:

attach asy 0x3f8 4 ax25 tnc0 2048 256 4800

In this example, *NOS* uses an asynchronous port ("asy"), computer port COM1 ("0x3f8"), which is connected to an AX.25 TNC in the KISS mode ("ax25"). The name of the port is "tnc0" and it operates with a maximum buffer of 2048 bytes, a maximum packet length of 256 bytes, at 4800 baud. Although attach is most likely already preset for your computer, you may still wish to change the last parameter, that is, the data rate. It may be set to any data rate you wish to use for communications between your computer and TNC (not the on-the-air data rate).

The route parameter determines where your packets go after they are transmitted by your radio. The routing table that is set up using the route parameter causes your packets to be transmitted directly to the destination station or to an intermediary station that will relay the packet to the destination station. It is the same concept as a direct connection versus a connection via a digipeater or network node. Routing is complicated, so I will suggest the simplest way to set up your routing table and later you can make changes to adapt the table to suit your needs. First, set the route parameter as follows:

route add default tnc0

This setting causes all packets to be sent to the destination station without interception and transmission by an intermediary station. Now, if there is a station that you wish to contact via an intermediary station, you add a line to the routing table in the following format:

• route add [(*IP address of destination station*)] tnc0 [(*IP address of intermediary station*)], e.g., route add [44.56.0.131] tnc0 [44.88.0.26]

If other stations require intermediary station routing, you simply add their routes to the table.

When you are ready to TCP/IP with a station, your TCP/IP software will look up that station in the routing table to see how the packets to that station are routed. If a station is not listed in the routing table, then the TCP/IP software uses the default routing scheme, i.e., the direct connection with no intermediary stations.

Obviously, the routing table will get long quickly after you get on the air and discover who is out there that needs intermediary routing. To avoid this ever-lengthening routing table problem, your TCP/IP software documentation discusses other ways to set up the routing table, but, for now, I want to get you on the air as quickly and simply as possible and what I have described is one way to do it.

After you have made these changes, save the *autoexec.**** file because we are finished with it.

alias

Alias simplifies addressing mail. The format of an ALIAS entry is (*alias*) (*host name of alias*), for example, stan wa1lou@wa1lou.ampr.org. This entry saves time by permitting you to address mail to WA1LOU by telling the software to send the mail to "stan," rather than to "wa1lou@wa1lou.ampr.org."

Alias also helps to organize mail received at your station. Some of the mail I receive is addressed to "wa1lou@wa1lou" and some of it is addressed to "stan@wa1lou." Depending on how I have set up the user parameter of my mailing software, it allows me to either read mail addressed to "wa1lou@wa1lou" or "stan@wa1lou," but not both. To get around this, I have "stan wa1lou" in my *Alias* file to force my mailing software to treat mail addressed to "stan@wa1lou" the same as mail addressed to "wa1lou@wa1lou" ("Stan" is an alias of "wa1lou").

hosts.net or domain.txt

Hosts.net and *domain.txt* cross-reference the host name of a station with its IP address, so when you communicate with another station, you don't have to remember its IP address, just its host name. The format of a *hosts.net* entry is (*IP address*) (*host name*) (*other host name*), for example, 44.88.4.8 wa1lou wa1lou.ampr.org. The format of a *domain.txt* entry is (*host name*) IN A (*IP address*), for example, wa1lou.ampr.org IN A 44.88.4.8. These entries allow me to talk to myself by entering "wa1lou" or "wa1lou.ampr.org," rather than "44.88.4.8."

For starters, make an entry for your own station and any other local TCP/IP stations you know. Later, you can get a full-blown *hosts.net* or *domain.txt* file for your region from one of the local "veteran" TCP/IP stations.

\public or \pub

The \public or \pub subdirectory contains all the files that you want other stations to be able to access. The only thing to remember is that for compatibility with the majority of TCP/IP users (the majority are using MS-DOS computers), the file names contained in \public or \pub should follow the MS-DOS file name structure, that is, a maximum of 8 characters followed by a period and a maximum of 3 characters, for example, *GOODSTUF.TCP* or *GOODS.IP* but not *GOODSTUFF.TCPIP*.

\finger

The \finger subdirectory contains short files that can be read by other stations that use the finger command to access your station. For example, a 16-line file named *WA1LOU.txt* in my \finger subdirectory describes me and my packet radio station. If a station invokes the command:

finger WA1LOU@WA1LOU

the file named *WA1LOU.txt* will be sent back to that station. For starters, set up a similar file in your \finger subdirectory.

The Moment of Truth!

Now, let's see if all this works. Run your TCP/IP program and, after its prompt appears, enter:

finger (your call sign)@(your call sign)

Your TCP/IP program will read and display the file that you just created in your \finger subdirectory. If that *is* what happens, let's see next if it works on the air because fingering yourself is an operation that occurs within the confines of your computer; nothing is sent over the air.

Try and get that full-blown *hosts.net* or *domain.txt* file from another station. KE3Z is the most veteran TCP/IP station in these parts, so I will get the file from him using my TCP/IP software's File Transfer Protocol (or FTP).

First, I want to test the path between my station and KE3Z, so I invoke the ping command at the TCP/IP software's command prompt, by typing:

ping ke3z <CR>

My system pings KE3Z's system and my terminal displays:

44.88.0.1: echo reply id 0 seq 61531, 7000 ms

KE3Z's IP address is 44.88.0.1 and 7000 ms is the amount of time it took to send the ping from my station to KE3Z. Now that I know that KE3Z is on the air, I will initiate an FTP session, at the command prompt, by typing:

ftp ke3z <CR>

If all goes well, my computer will indicate that a session has been "Established" and that KE3Z is ready for me to log on. To log on, you must supply a user name and password. Most systems allow you to log on using "anonymous" for a user name and your call sign for a password. After entering the user name and password, you will receive a message that you are logged on.

Next, send "dir" to get a list of the contents (a "directory") of the public subdirectory. If the directory contains a *hosts.net* or *domain.txt* file, I get a copy by entering "get" followed by the name of the hosts.net or domain.txt file. After entering the get command, my computer indicates that a data connection for retrieval of the file is opening, then displays nothing while the file is actually being transferred. The file transfer can go on for quite a while. The keying of my transmitter is the only indication that anything is happening. while the actual transfer is occurring, I can open another session to perform other tasks simultaneously.

When the transfer is completed, my computer displays "Get complete" followed by the number of bytes transferred and the "File sent OK" message. At the prompt, I enter "close" to end the FTP session and log off KE3Z.

That's the tip of the TCP/IP iceberg! There is a lot more you can do with TCP/IP (see the sidebar titled "TCP/IP User Commands"), but this should get you started on the right path. Meanwhile, I will be waiting for your TCP/IP packets (sent to 44.88.4.8)!

TEXNET

As its name implies, TexNet originated in Texas with the Texas Packet Radio Society (TPRS). Today, TexNets exist in various parts of the U.S., including Texas, Oklahoma, Arkansas, Indiana, Michigan and New Mexico.

TexNet allows users to communicate via a high-speed UHF network using plain vanilla TNCs. While users communicate with their local TexNet nodes at 1200 bits/s, the network conducts inter-nodal communications at 9600 bit/s on 70 cm. This high speed network is transparent to the users, but results in a higher user data throughput than can be achieved over a 1200-bit/s network.

How to Use TexNet

To use TexNet, you first connect with a local network node. You accomplish this by using the Connect command followed by the call sign of the local node and the appropriate SSID. Different SSIDs provide different services as delineated in the following list.

SSID	Service
0	Digipeating
2 and 3	Conference bridging
4	Network access
5	Local node terminal interfacing, also known as Local Node Console
6	Packet Message System or PMS (TexNet's PBBS service)
8 and 9	Crossband digipeating

If you wish to use TexNet to communicate with another station, you access the network by using the Connect command followed by the call sign of the local node and the SSID of 4, for example:

cmd: Connect *LOCAL*-4 <CR>

where *LOCAL* is the call sign of the local node. After you connect with a local node, you will receive the "Network Cmd" prompt. At that prompt, you can ask the network to set up communications with the other station by invoking the Connect command (with your TNC in the Converse Mode), followed by the call sign of the other station and the alias of that station's local node, for example:

Network Cmd: Connect *OTHRSTN@OTHRNODE* <CR>

TexNet User Commands

A description of each TexNet user command follows. Most of the commands may be invoked by entering only the first letter of the command. Note that these commands are used only after you have connected with a TexNet node (using your TNC's "Connect" command).

? – Causes a node to send you a list the user commands.

Bye – Disconnects you from a node.

Connect *x*@*y* – Causes a node to initiate a connection with a user whose call sign is *x* at a node whose name is *y*.

Connect *x* v *y1 y2*@*z* – Causes a node to initiate a connection with a user whose call sign is *x* via one or two digipeaters whose call signs are *y1* and *y2* at a node whose name is *z*.

Connect *x*@*y,n* – Causes a node to initiate a connection with a user whose call sign is *x* via port *n* at a node whose name is *y*.

Connect CQ@*x* – Causes a node whose name is *x* to send "CQ."

Help – Causes a node to list its user commands.

Locations – Causes a node to list the 7-character names of all of the network nodes.

Message – Causes a node to initiate a connection to the Packet Message System (PMS). (The PMS uses a subset of the WØRLI Mailbox command set.)

Message@*x* – Causes a node to initiate a connection to the Packet Message System (PMS) at a node whose name is *x*. (The PMS uses a subset of the WØRLI Mailbox command set.)

Statistics@*x* – Causes a node whose name is *x* to list node statistics that have been accumulated since midnight.

Statistics Y@*x* – Causes a node whose name is *x* to list the node statistics that had been accumulated the previous day.

Weather – Causes a node to initiate a connection to the weather server module of the Packet Message System (PMS).

where *OTHRSTN* is the call sign of the other station and *OTHRNODE* is the call sign or alias of the other station's local node (local node alias' are usually based on city names). Your local node commences communications with the other node at 9600 bit/s trying to establish a connection with the other station. At this high speed, it will not be long before communications are established (assuming that the other station is currently active on the other node's 2-meter frequency).

Local Services

In addition to high speed network communications, TexNet provides users with a variety of other useful services. Users access these services by invoking the Connect command (again with your TNC in the Converse Mode) followed by the call sign of the node and the appropriate SSID. The following services are accessible via TexNet:

Digipeating – When all else fails, TexNet provides the old standby: standard AX.25 digipeating. Normally, you should avoid this function in favor of the network and conference bridging functions.

Conference Bridging – Each TexNet node supports two independent local conference bridges (SSIDs 2 and 3). These bridges allow three or more stations at a local node to communicate with each other in roundtable fashion. (This function does not support conferencing between stations located at different nodes in the network.)

Packet Message System (PMS) – Typically, each TexNet network is supported by one *PMS*. One *PMS* per network eliminates message forwarding which is one of the prime culprits that bogs down throughput in an AX.25 multi-PBBS network. Because there is only one *PMS* in the network, you can also access it from any node on the network by simply invoking the Message command at the Network Cmd prompt (refer to the accompanying sidebar, "TexNet User Commands," for a list of other user commands that are available at the Network Cmd prompt).

Local Node Console – This function allows you to access the node "directly," that is, by means of the node's controller: the TexNet Network Control Processor (NCP) board.

Crossband Digipeating – If other channels are supported by the local node, this function allows you to access them.

Hardware Considerations

The basic TexNet node consists of the following hardware: a Network Control Processor (NCP), modems (9600 and 1200 bit/s depending on configuration), a 2-meter radio, a backbone radio capable of operating at 9600 bit/s and miscellaneous components including a vertical antenna for 2 meters, a directional antenna for the backbone, splitters, feed line, etc.

The NCP is a Z80 microprocessor-based device that dispenses the TexNet services. It comes in three flavors: NCP 2.1, NCP-PC 1.0 and TNC TexNet.

NCP 2.1, the original TexNet NCP, supports three ports and a local console. It contains 1200-baud AFSK and 9600-baud FSK modems and can use a hard disk controller for PMS operation. Most nodes currently in operation use this board.

NCP-PC is an IBM XT/AT class plug-in card that supports four ports and software development hardware. It requires external modems for the radio connections. The purposes of this card were (1) to create a development card for testing code and (2) allow a direct interface to a computer for more complicated user services at the network level.

TNC-TexNet is firmware that allows a TNC to operate as a single-port TexNet node. It creates intermediate backbone links by using external 9600-baud modems that provides "thin" network routes, for example, through areas of West Texas.

CONCLUSION

The success of amateur packet radio lies in a packet radio network that is a well-oiled machine. If the network machinery runs poorly, packet radio will come to a grinding halt. That is why the work of the various groups and individuals described in this chapter need the support and cooperation of every Amateur Radio packet user. They are the ones oiling the network machinery. Packet radio's existence depends on them!

TCP/IP User Commands

A list of the TCP/IP user commands follows. Most of the commands may be invoked by entering only the first or first two letters of the full command name, for example, D for the Disconnect command and AR for the ARP command. (These commands are based on the *KA9Q Internet Protocol Package*, *NET/Mac*, Macintosh Version 2.3 by Adam van Gaalen, PA2AGA.)

#$debug on
?|help
abort
addmenu *<string>*
adjustclock *<seconds>*
alerts [*0-5*]
appleshare [*<hostname> <path-to-mqueue>*]
arp
arp add *<hostid>*|*<address> ethernet|ax25|netrom|mac <ethernet address>*|*<call sign>*
arp drop *<hostid>*|*<address> ethernet|ax25|netrom|mac*
arp publish *<hostid>*|*<address> ethernet|ax25|netrom|mac <ethernet address>*|*<call sign>*
attach appletalk *<protocol type> <device>* arpa *<label> <rx bufsize> <mtu>*
attach asy|kpc4 *<address> <port* (*a* or *b*)*> slip|ax25|nrs <label> <buffers> <mtu> <speed>*
attach netrom
ax25 digipeat [*on|off*]
ax25 heard [*on|off|clear*]
ax25 maxframe [*<number of frames>*]
ax25 mycall [*<call sign>*]
ax25 paclen [*<number of bytes>*]
ax25 pthresh [*<number of bytes>*]
ax25 reset *<axcb>*
ax25 retry [*<number of retries>*]
ax25 status [*<axcb>*]
ax25 t1 [*<milliseconds>*]
ax25 t2 [*<milliseconds>*]
ax25 t3 [*<milliseconds>*]
ax25 window [*<number of bytes>*]
axtext [*<message>*]
beacon callsign [*<call sign>*]
beacon interval [*<seconds>*]
beacon message [*<message>*]
beacon set [*<interface>*]
beacon [*enable|disable*]
callbk *<databasename> <logfilename>* [*encoded|amsoft*]
callbookserver [*<hostname>*]
cd *<directory>*—ftp only —
cd [*<directory>*]

chat <*hostname*>|<*ip-number*>

close [<*session number*>]

cmdtoclipb [*on*|*off*]

connect <*interface*> <*call sign*> [<*digipeater*> ...]

console [*x y r c*]

ctext1 [<*message line 1*>]

ctext2 [<*message line 2*>]

date

dir [<*file*>|<*directory*> [<*local file*>]] — ftp only —

dir [<*file*>|<*directory*>]

disconnect [<*session number*>]

dontalias <*user*> [<*user*> ...]

echo [*refuse*|*accept*]

eol [*unix*|*standard*]

escape [<*character*>]

exit

finger <*user*>|<*user*>@<*hostid*>|@<*hostid*>

flow [*on*|*off*]

fontsize <*new fontsize*>

forward [<*interface*> <*interface*>]

ftext1 [<*message line 1*>]

ftext2 [<*message line 2*>]

ftp <*hostid*>|<*address*>

get <*remotefile*> [<*localfile*>]

help

hostfile [<*filename*>]

hostname [<*name*>]

ignorebadheaders [*on*|*off*]

inquire <*call sign*>

ip address [<*hostid*>|<*address*>]

ip heard [*on*|*off*|*clear*]

ip status

ip ttl [<*number*>]

is_es add <*hostid*>|<*address*> ax25 <*to whom*>

is_es drop <*hostid*>|<*address*> ax25 <*to whom*>

is_es [*enable*|*disable*]

kick <*session number*>

list [<*file*>|<*directory*> [<*local file*>]]

log [*stop*|<*filename*>]

ls [<*file*>|<*directory*> [<*local file*>]]

macb [*enable*|*disable*]

mbox [*y*|*n*|*?*]

mkdir <*directory*>

mode <*interface*> [*vc*|*datagram*]

netmacicons [*on*|*off*]

netrom acktime [<*milliseconds*>]

netrom bcnodes <*interface*>

netrom choketime [<*milliseconds*>]

netrom connect <*node*>
netrom interface <*interface*> <*alias*> <*quality*>
netrom irtt [<*milliseconds*>]
netrom kick <*&nrcb*>
netrom nodefilter add <*neighbor*> <*interface*>
netrom nodefilter drop <*neighbor*> <*interface*>
netrom nodefilter mode [*none*|*accept*|*reject*]
netrom nodetimer [<*seconds*>]
netrom obsotimer [<*seconds*>]
netrom qlimit [<*number of bytes*>]
netrom reset <*&nrcb*>
netrom retries [<*number of retries*>]
netrom route
netrom route add <*alias*> <*destination*> <*interface*> <*quality*>
    <*neighbor*>
netrom route drop <*destination*> <*neighbor*> <*interface*>
netrom route info <*destination*>
netrom status [<*&nrcb*>]
netrom ttl [<*number*>]
netrom verbose [*yes*|*no*]
netrom window [<*number*>]
nrstat
nrtext [<*message*>]
param <*interface*> <*data field*> <*value*>
pass <*password*>
perform [*clear*]|[<*command*> <*hh:mm*>|+<*delay*> [*once*]
    [<*dayofweek*>]]|[*permanent*]]
ping [[<*hostid*> [*reset*|<*seconds*>|<*packetsize*>*b*][<*packetsize*>]]|*clear*]
prompt [<*newprompt*>]
put <*localfile*> [<*remotefile*>]
pwd
quadralink [<*slot*> [*dma*]]
quit
rdate <*timehost*>
realtime [*on*|*off*]
reboot_on_bad_date
record <*filename*> [<*session*>]|*off*
remote [*-p* <*port#*>] [*-k* <*key*>] [*-a* <*hostid*>] <*hostid*> *reset*|*exit*|*kickme*
reset <*session number*>
resetsmtpto <*hostname*>
rip add <*hostid*>|<*address*> <*interface*> <*interval*> [<*flags*>]
rip addprivate <*hostid*>|<*address*> <*interface*> <*interval*> [<*flags*>]
rip addrefuse <*gateway*>
rip drop <*hostid*>|<*address*> <*interface*>
rip droprefuse <*gateway*>
rip init
rip status

rip trace [*on*|*off*]
rmdir *<file>*|*<directory>*
route
route add *<hostid>*[/*<bits>*]|*default* *<interface>* [*<gateway hostid>*]
    [*<metric>*]
route drop *<hostid>*[/*<bits>*]|*default*
route expanded
route window *<hostname>* *<tcp-window-size>*
rtntoses [*on*|*off*]
sesscreen [*<width>*[*<length>*]]
session [*<session number>*]
sleep *<seconds>*
smtp gateway [*<hostid>*|*<address>*]
smtp kick
smtp maxclients [*<number>*]
smtp mode [*queue*|*route*]
smtp multi [*on*|*off*]
smtp ndays [*<number of days>*]
smtp timer [*<seconds>*]
smtp trace [*<trace flag>*]
smtp vm
source *<filename>*
sourcewhendone *<hostname>* *<source-filename>*
start *discard*|*echo*|*finger*|*ftp*|*remote*|*smtp*|*telnet* [*port#*]
stop *discard*|*echo*|*finger*|*ftp*|*remote*|*smtp*|*telnet*
tcp active
tcp extended
tcp irtt [*<milliseconds>*]
tcp kick *<number>*|*<tcb address>*
tcp mrtt [*<milliseconds>*]
tcp mss [*<number of bytes>*]
tcp reset *<number>*|*<tcb address>*
tcp rtt *<tcb address>* *<milliseconds>*
tcp status [*<number>*|*<tcb address>*]
tcp window [*<number of bytes>*]
telnet *<hostid>*|*<address>*
time
title *<new consolewindow title>*
trace [*<interface>* [*<flags>*] [*x y r c*] [*<to filename>*]]
traceonly [*all*|*<call sign>*]
traces [*<interface>* [*<flags>*] [*x y r c*] [*<to filename>*]]
ttylink *<hostid>*|*<address>*
type [*a*|*ascii*|*i*|*image*|*b*|*binary*|l *<logical bytesize>*]
tzone [*<time zone>* [*<offset>*]]
udp status
upload *<filename>* [*<session>*]
user *<user>*
whois *<info>*

8

HF Communications

HF Amateur Radio communication, whatever the mode, means DX. The long-distance propagation provided by the HF radio spectrum makes transcontinental and transoceanic communications possible. DX communication also plays an important role in the overall packet radio scheme. Long-distance packet radio communications provide the means for packet radio experimenters in different countries to exchange ideas and information concerning amateur packet radio technology. In addition, packet radio mail is forwarded and delivered over long distances using the HF bands.

300-BAUD EQUIPMENT

Operating HF packet radio is quite different from VHF and UHF packet radio operating. One significant difference is that the authorized maximum data rate in the HF radio spectrum is lower than in the VHF and UHF spectrum. The maximum data rate permitted by present FCC regulations below 28 MHz is 300 bauds. On 10 meters, 1200-baud packet radio is permitted.

Besides the lower data rate, another significant difference is the method of generating the packet radio signals. On VHF, packet radio typically uses audio tones applied to the microphone input of an FM transmitter to generate an AFSK signal. On HF, the audio tones are applied to the microphone input of a single-sideband suppressed-carrier transmitter to generate what is essentially an FSK signal. At 300 bauds, TAPR TNCs use 1600-Hz and 1800-Hz tones (200-Hz shift), rather than the Bell 202 tones (1000-Hz shift) used at VHF and above.

Most of the TNCs manufactured today may be used at 300 bauds or 1200 bauds simply by flipping a switch or invoking a software command. The majority of older TNCs (the TNC 1 and original TNC 2) included only the Bell 202 VHF/UHF standard modem, if they included a modem at all. The owners of those older TNCs either had to make modifications to the internal modem, if there was one, or add an external HF-compatible modem.

Modification of the modems in the TNC 1 and TNC 2 requires changing the values of one capacitor and one resistor (change TNC 1 C21 or TNC 2 C54 to 0.01 μF and TNC 1 R46 or TNC 2 R93 to 220 kΩ). After the components are changed, the modem must be calibrated, and the radio-port data rate must be changed to 300 bauds (TNC 1 command Hbaud 300 or TNC 2 DIP switch position 6 ON). The disadvantage of modifying the internal modem is that the TNC cannot then be used for VHF and UHF operation without modifying and calibrating the modem again.

Adding an external modem for HF operation provides a more convenient alternative. Commercial HF modems are simple to install and use. The problem is that commercial HF modems are scarce. Various manufacturers sold them five years ago, but almost none do today, so you will have to do your HF modem shopping in the used market.

If you do find a commercial HF modem, installation requires proper cabling between a TNC and the modem. After the proper connections are made, switching between the external HF modem and the TNC's internal modem is as simple as engaging or disengaging a front panel push-button switch and changing the TNC's radio-port data rate. In addition, each manufacturer claims that the designs of their external HF modems are optimized for HF operation so they provide better performance than a modified internal TNC modem.

TUNING A SIGNAL

One of the most difficult parts of HF packet radio operation is properly tuning a received signal. On VHF and UHF, tuning is simply a matter of turning the transceiver's frequency selector to a known active packet radio channel and waiting for a packet to be displayed on your terminal.

On HF, tuning is more difficult. Tune your HF receiver very slowly across that part of the band that contains known packet radio activity. Tune in as small an increment as possible (10-Hz increments are desirable) until your terminal begins displaying packets. When you tune on HF, do not change frequency until you hear the end of a packet. If you shift frequency in mid-packet, it is likely that the packet will not be received properly and will not be displayed on your terminal even if you were on the correct frequency before or after the frequency change. Remember, each packet must be received correctly from beginning to end before the TNC will send it to your terminal for display.

Most TNCs that include HF modems (and most external commercial HF modems) include tuning indicators to simplify proper HF tuning. For example, some tuning indicators consist of a multiple-segment LED bar display. You tune your receiver until the maximum number of segments are lit equally in either direction from the center of the display. Using a tuning indicator is much easier than adjusting the receiver's frequency in 10-Hz steps until a packet is successfully displayed.

POINT-TO-POINT COMMUNICATIONS

Most HF packet radio communications are *point-to-point*. Very few digipeaters or network nodes are active on HF. There are several reasons for this, including the fact that FCC regulations do not allow unattended digipeater operation on HF. Another important reason is that an operating digipeater or node is technically passing third-party traffic. If you connect through a digipeater or node to a station in a country that does not have a third-party traffic agreement with the United States, the operator of the digipeater or node is in violation of FCC rules. HF digipeater and node operation also compounds the *hidden transmitter* problem, where your TNC cannot hear a station (or stations) that the digipeater or node can hear. This leads to collision problems and general confusion. For all these reasons, it is best to disable your TNC's digipeater function on HF and to avoid using any active digipeaters or nodes you may hear.

The lack of digipeaters and network nodes on HF is really not a problem. On HF, point-to-point communications means interstate or international communications depending on the time of day, time of year, operating frequency and the number of active sunspots.

Although HF provides long-distance propagation for packet radio, conditions can vary widely. Anyone who has operated on HF knows that one minute you may be in contact with a station half way around the world with excellent signals at both ends, and the next minute you may be talking to yourself as propagation shifts and closes

HF TNC Parameters

When a TNC is turned on for the first time or whenever the "Reset" command is invoked, all of the TNC's selectable parameters are set to their default selections, which are optimized for VHF and UHF operation. To operate successfully on HF, certain critical parameters must be changed from the default values. Those parameters are listed here to provide a quick reference for configuring the TNC for HF operation.

Radio port data rate:

Below 50 MHz, 300 baud:

TNC 1: Hbaud = 300

TNC 2: DIP switch position 6 = ON

28.0 - 50.0 MHz, 1200 baud:

TNC 1: Hbaud = 1200

TNC 2: DIP switch position 7 = ON

MAXframe = 1 (maximum number of outstanding unacknowledged packets)

Paclen = 64 or less (number of bytes in each packet)

DIGIpeat = OFF (disable TNC's digipeater function)

DWait = 0 (a digipeater timing function, unnecessary on HF)

TXdelay = minimum radio receive-to-transmit mode turnaround time

AXDelay = 0 (an unnecessary voice repeater timing function)

AXHang = 0 (an unnecessary voice repeater timing function)

the path to the other station. To compensate somewhat for the vagaries of HF propagation, certain critical TNC parameters may be changed. You cannot run a TNC in the same configuration on HF as on VHF or UHF where propagation is more stable. The accompanying sidebar summarizes the critical TNC parameters that should be changed for HF operation, while Chapter 4 fully describes how to select these parameters.

THE DX CONNECTION

Working packet radio DX is not much different than working DX in any other mode. You tune to an active HF packet radio channel with the monitoring function enabled and check for DX call signs. If you hear a DX station that you would like to contact, you wait patiently for the DX station to finish his current contact. After the DX station disconnects, you may send a connect request to that station; assuming that the propagation path is reciprocal, you should be able to make a DX connection.

With the assistance of HF propagation, it is now possible to make packet radio contacts with stations in all 50 states. To recognize this achievement, the ARRL offers the Worked-All-States (WAS) award to any operator who can submit written confirmation of packet radio contacts with stations in all 50 states (the District of Columbia counts as Maryland). The proof of contact (usually a QSL card) must state that the mode used to make the contact was packet radio and that two-way communication was established. Contacts made through repeater or network devices do not count. Anyone interested in applying for the packet radio WAS should send a self-addressed, stamped envelope addressed to ARRL/WAS, 225 Main Street, Newington, CT 06111, to obtain a WAS application form.

MAIL FORWARDING

Besides DX contacts, another significant HF packet radio activity is the mail-forwarding function performed by various PBBS stations throughout the United States. The mail-forwarding function is the means by which messages uploaded to local PBBSs are transferred from one area of the country to another. Much mail-forwarding takes place on VHF and UHF, but long-distance forwarding usually involves some use of HF. Forwarding long-distance mail on HF is quicker (fewer hops) and in some cases it is the only way that the message can be transferred. For example, to forward a message from one coast to the other coast, it would take many VHF and UHF mail-forwarding stations to relay that message to its destination. On HF, however, two mail-forwarding stations (one on each coast) can perform that same task. There may also be some gaps in the VHF and UHF path needed to relay the message from coast to coast. HF relays can fill the gaps. Refer to Figure 8-1 for a comparison of HF and VHF long-distance mail forwarding.

At this time, the HF network of mail-forwarding relay stations is fairly stable. Each mail-forwarding station has a list of all of the other mail-forwarding stations and they are usually configured to connect with those stations only. If you attempt to make a connection with a mail-forwarding station, you will be summarily disconnected. These stations are similar to dedicated digipeater or node stations. Their only purpose is to relay messages to other mail-forwarding stations; they cannot be used by other stations for other purposes.

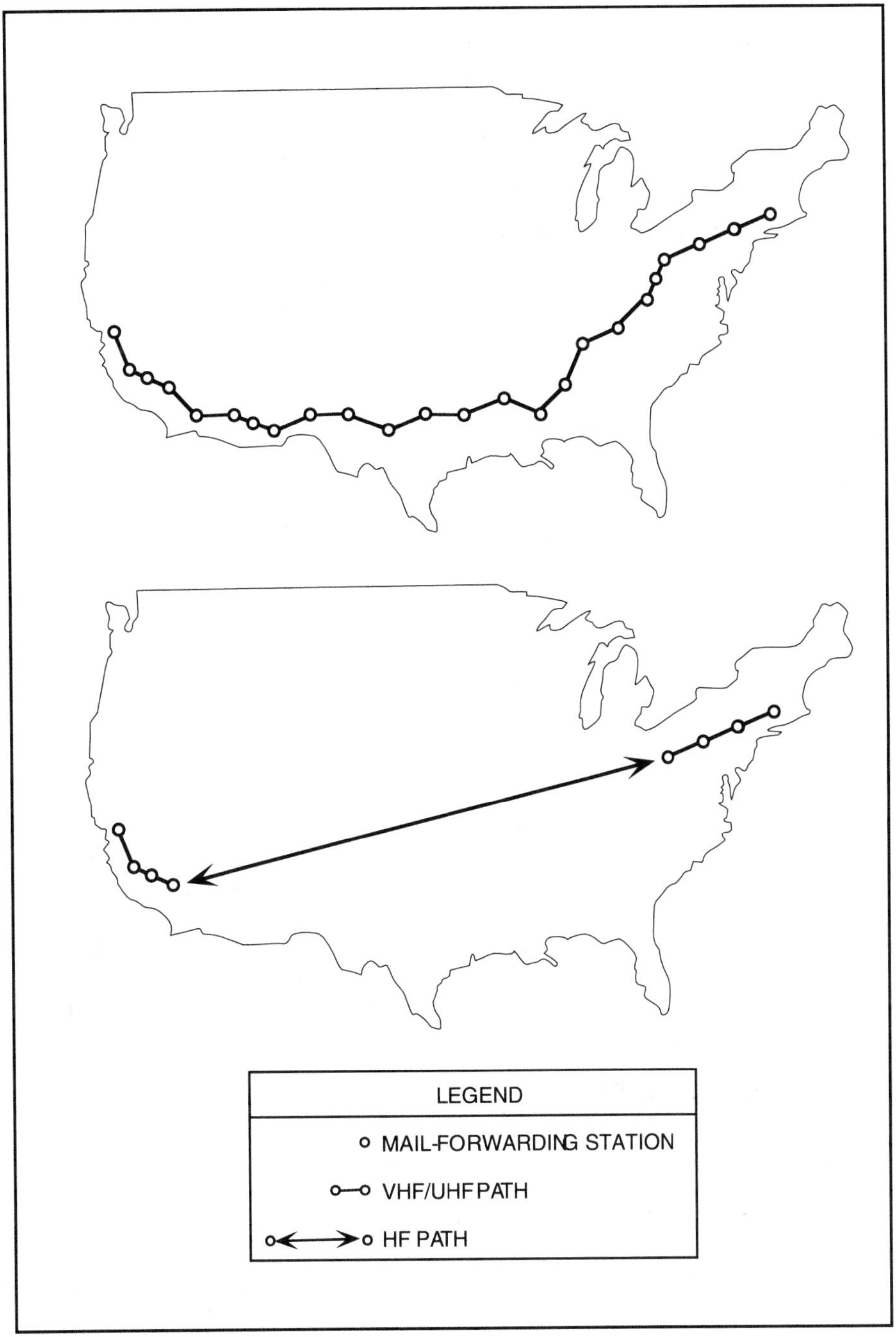

Figure 8-1—Mail can be forwarded over long distances on HF much more easily than on VHF.

Not only is the mail-forwarding function performed automatically by the computer at each mail-forwarding station, but the operator of a mail-forwarding station can leave his station running on the air all of the time because FCC regulations now permit unattended operation below 50 MHz. To promote the unimpeded flow of the mail-forwarding process, you should not try to connect with these mail-forwarding stations, nor should you transmit on the mail-forwarding channels.

GOOD OPERATING PROCEDURES

As we mentioned in Chapter 6 on basic operating procedures, packet radio operating requires a knowledge of good operating practices, just like any other Amateur Radio communications mode. It's important to learn the procedures before you transmit.

Suggested Operating Frequencies

Over the years, various parts of the HF Amateur Radio bands have become the home for different modes of communications. RTTY, SSTV, DX, traffic nets, beacons and other amateur operations all have a place that they can call home on the HF bands. Most amateurs respect these "gentlemen's agreements" and do not operate one mode in those portions of the bands that are dedicated to other modes of operation. Similarly, packet radio has settled on some HF frequencies that are recognized by others as intended for packet radio only.

At this time, 20 meters is the most active HF packet radio band. Originally, 20-meter HF packet radio operators chose 14.103 MHz as the frequency for their activity because it was just above another digital mode of communications, 20-meter RTTY activity between 14.070 and 14.099 MHz. As it turned out, 14.103 MHz was too close to the 20-meter DX beacons operating on 14.100 MHz. Although the beacons generally did not hamper packet radio operations, the packet radio activity did interfere with the DX beacons, under certain circumstances. If the packet radio operators were right on 14.103 and the DX operators used narrow CW filters, there was no interference. If the packet radio operators drifted down towards the beacons or the DX operators were using wider SSB filters, however, it was possible for interference to occur. After a hue and cry was sounded by DXers around the world, the packet radio operators became aware of the problem and many stations moved their operations off 14.103 MHz. Table 8-1 is a suggested band plan for HF.

Relief from Congestion

If you use an HF calling frequency to establish a connection, it is good operating practice to move the contact to another, less active frequency. The HF calling frequencies are often very congested. There is a high potential for packet collisions and, with the constant changes in HF propagation, these crowded channels get very confusing. As the propagation shifts, connected stations can no longer hear each other and the frequency becomes full of repeated packets seeking acknowledgments they will never receive. It is hard enough to contend with other connected transmissions without adding these unacknowledged packets to the congestion, so it is best to move to a quieter frequency after making a connection on the calling frequency.

Table 8-1
Suggested HF Frequencies for Packet Radio Activity

80 Meters: 3.620-3.635 MHz

40 Meters: 7.100-7.105 MHz

30 Meters: 10.140-10.150 MHz

20 Meters: 14.095-14.0995 MHz, 14.1005-14.112 MHz

17 Meters: 18.105-18.110 MHz

15 Meters: 21.090-21.100 MHz

12 Meters: 24.925-24.930 MHz

10 Meters: 28.120-28.189 MHz

CQs and Beacons

The general rules concerning packet radio CQs and beacons that were discussed in Chapter 6 apply to HF packet radio operations.

Calling CQ plays a more important role on HF than it does on VHF and UHF. Every hour of the day a different part of the world may be available on HF. You never know who is monitoring the frequency and calling CQ may be the only way to flush out a contact. Beacons can also be used to flush out a DX contact, but calling CQ is preferred. The CQ call gets the job done, and it is usually shorter than a beacon. Unless you have a good reason to transmit a beacon; if you are operating a contest, for example, (CQ Field Day) or a special event station (CQ from the State Fair), stick with the traditional CQ.

CONCLUSION

This chapter described the fundamental operating procedures for HF packet radio communications. With a TNC connected to a low-band transceiver, you are now ready to chase DX digital-style. There are a lot of potential international connections out there. Good luck and good DX!

9

Bulletin Boards

Time-shifting packet radio was not invented by H. G. Wells. Actually, it was invented by Hank Oredson, WØRLI, back in 1984. Since that time, time shifting has taken on various shapes and sizes to be one of the driving forces that has made packet radio grow so quickly.

TIME-SHIFTING COMMUNICATIONS

Time-shifting communication sounds space-aged and very complicated, but it is actually fairly simple to define. In fact, it is not even new. RTTY operators have been using time-shifting communications for a long time. Simply defined, time-shifting communication is the function of transferring information between two people who may not be present on the air at the same time. In other words, using time-shifting communications permits me to send information to you while you are involved in some other activity, yet I can be reasonably assured that you will receive the information (sooner or later).The *packet radio bulletin board system* (*PBBS*) is used to time-shift packet radio communications.

BULLETIN BOARDS AND MAILBOXES

During the personal-computer age, the telephone-line *bulletin board system (BBS)* has become very common. Simply connect a modem between your computer and your telephone line and you can dial up thousands of different BBSs around the world. Using a BBS, you can read messages stored on the BBS by other users and you can store messages addressed to the other users. You can also download public-domain computer programs that are stored on a BBS to run on your computer.

The PBBS works essentially the same way as a BBS. The only difference is that instead of connecting a modem to your computer and your telephone line as you would to access a BBS, you connect a TNC to your computer and your transceiver to access a PBBS (refer to Fig 9-1). Another difference is that to access a BBS, you must pur-

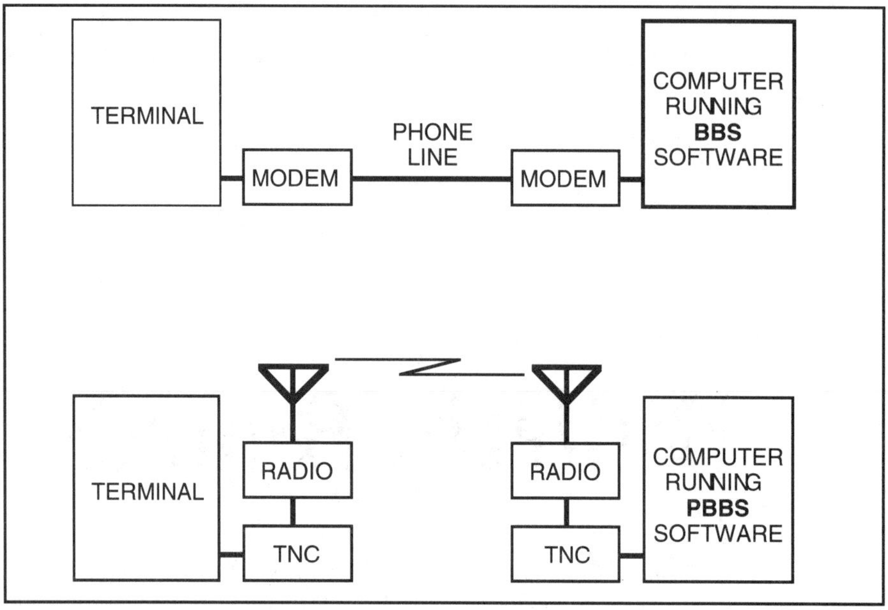

Fig 9-1—The differences between a telephone-line BBS and a packet-radio BBS.

chase the telephone service from your local telephone company; to access a PBBS, you need a valid Amateur Radio license.

A PBBS is a packet radio station that is interfaced to a computer that runs software to perform BBS functions over the airwaves.

Another means of time-shifting communications is provided by the packet radio *mailbox*. A packet radio mailbox is similar to a PBBS, but the term "mailbox" is generally accepted to mean a message receiving and sending system for one station rather than a bulletin board for all stations Your packet radio mailbox allows you to store messages to other stations who might check into your mailbox. It also permits other stations to send messages to you via your mailbox. Unlike a PBBS, however, your mailbox does not provide a means for amateurs to send messages to other stations.

Whether a PBBS or a mailbox is used, time-shifting packet radio communication is a very powerful communications tool of the computer age. Let's find out how it got started.

ONE MAN'S TRASH IS ANOTHER MAN'S TREASURE

The Xerox 820-I was a computer, introduced around 1980, used a Zilog Z80 central processing unit (CPU) and ran the CP/M operating system. It featured 64k bytes of RAM, two 8-bit parallel ports, two serial ports, a disk controller and an 80-column by 24-line video display, all on a single printed-circuit board.

In the early 1980s, Xerox discontinued selling the "820" and sold off the remainder that they had on hand as surplus. Their warehouse in Texas was the source for the surplus computer and they could be had for as little as $50 per board!

Hank Oredson, WØRLI, wrote a software package for the 820 that permitted it to function as a PBBS (and more). Besides the normal functions that you would expect to find in any BBS, such as the ability to send and receive messages and files, Hank added two features that made his BBS even more powerful.

One feature took advantage of the two serial ports provided by the 820. With a TNC connected to each port, Hank's software permitted a user connected to the TNC on one port to communicate through the TNC connected on the other port. Assuming that each TNC was connected to radio equipment operating on different frequencies, this system provided a gateway from one frequency to the other (refer to Fig 9-2 for

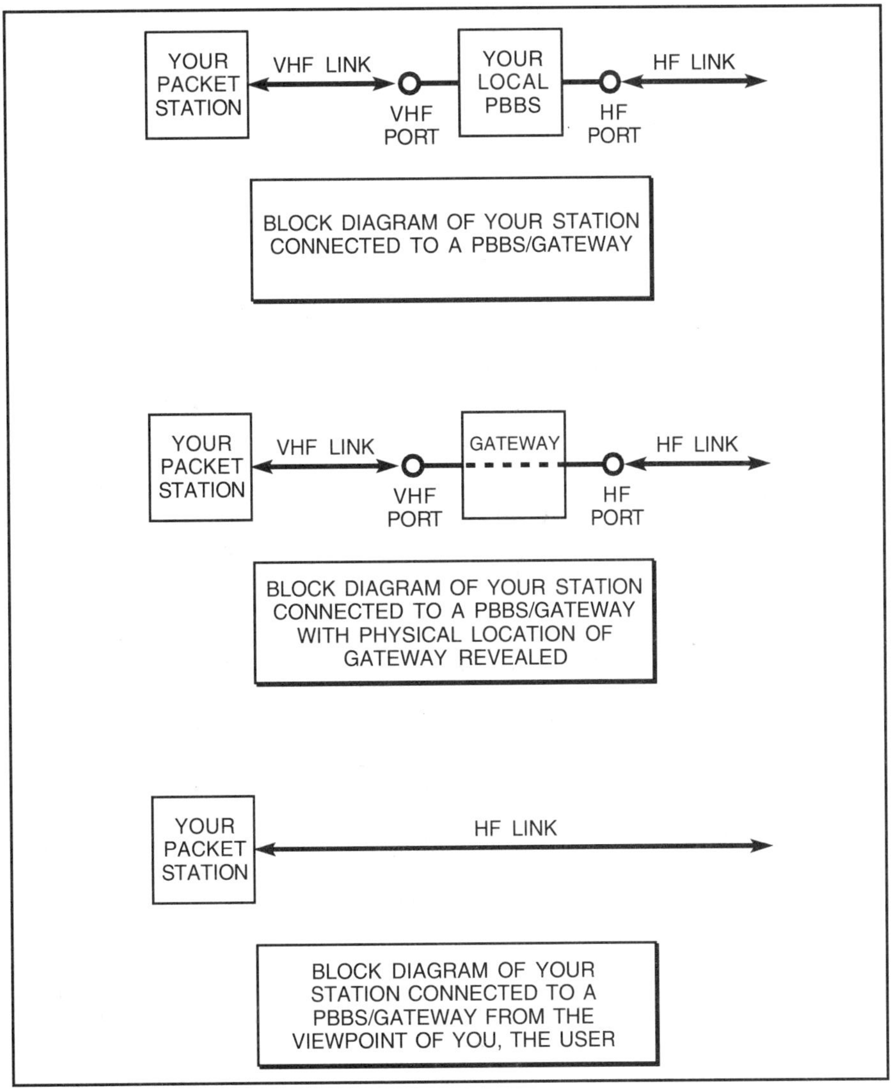

Fig 9-2—The WØRLI Mailbox gateway function.

an illustration of the gateway function). For example, if the TNC on one port was connected to a 2-meter transceiver and the TNC on the other port was connected to an HF transceiver, a PBBS user on 2 meters could use the gateway to make packet radio connections on HF.

Another feature created a rudimentary packet radio network for the automatic forwarding of messages between PBBSs. This mail-forwarding function allows PBBS users to send mail to the users of other PBBSs.

When addressing the mail, the user includes the call sign of the intended recipient of the mail and the call sign and location of the PBBS where the intended recipient receives mail (the intended recipient's *home PBBS*). Whenever the PBBS has mail to send to another PBBS, it consults a routing table that lists the path to the destination PBBS. When a path is found, the PBBS automatically sends the message to the first PBBS in the path. Each PBBS hands the message off to the next PBBS in the path, and eventually the message is delivered to the destination PBBS.

BEYOND THE 820

The WØRLI PBBS spread throughout packet radio. Wherever there was a pocket of packet radio activity, there was likely to be a WØRLI PBBS in operation. The 820 computer was inexpensive and the software was free. Hank not only gave his software away, but he continued to improve it. As each new version appeared, more and more WØRLI PBBSs hit the air. There was only one problem: the source of surplus 820 boards began to dry up. By mid-1985, the warehouse in Texas was unable to supply enough "new" surplus boards to meet the demand.

More operators wanted to set up PBBSs, so Jeff Jacobsen, WA7MBL, decided to meet this demand by writing PBBS software for the IBM PC. WA7MBL's PBBS was compatible with WØRLI's version and as IBM PC *clones* got cheaper and cheaper, WA7MBL's PBBS became a more and more viable alternative to the WØRLI version. Admittedly, the most inexpensive PC clone was still more expensive than a surplus 820, but at least the PC clones were readily available (and expandable). The PC clone also provided the ability to store a lot more information than was possible with the 820. Anyone who runs a PBBS will tell you that there is never too much storage capacity on the PBBS computer, so the WA7MBL PBBS was a blessing in this regard.

Having run out of computer once, WØRLI decided to embark on a new PBBS project that would not be tied to any one computer. With the help of David Toth, VE3GYQ, Hank wrote a new version of the PBBS in the computer language called "C." Programs written in C are said to be very "portable"; they may be run with only minor modifications on any computer that can handle C. Hank and David finished their C PBBS in late 1986, and it ran on the ever-present IBM PCs and PC clones.

Meanwhile, folks throughout packet-radioland were not letting the grass grow under their feet. Instead, they were busy writing PBBS and mailbox software for their own personal computers. The end result was a variety of PBBS and mailbox software for various popular computers including the Commodore 64, the IBM PC, the Radio Shack/Tandy Color Computer, the Radio Shack/Tandy TRS-80 Models I and III, and even the portable Radio Shack/Tandy TRS-80 Model 100! Some of these programs were compatible with the WØRLI/WA7MBL PBBSs and some were not.

Through the late 1980s and early 1990s, the prices of PC clones tumbled, while

PBBS Software

A variety of PBBS software is available for the IBM PC and its clones. Much of the software may be obtained from the following sources: by downloading from CompuServe's HamNet (Library 9), by ftp'ing via the Internet from the following sites: ftp.ucsd.edu or oak.oakland.edu and by mail on disk from TAPR (8987-309 E. Tanque Verde Rd, Tucson, AZ 85749-9399, phone 817-383-0000, fax 817-566-2544). Your local ham radio landline BBS may have the software, too. A list of the available software follows.

AA4RE BBS—This program is a multiple connection PBBS that was written by Roy Engehausen, AA4RE.

APLink—Vic Poor, W5SMM, wrote this AMTOR mailbox and WØRLI/WA7MBL-compatible packet radio BBS software.

ARES/Data—This software is a multiple-connection, multiport database and conference bridge designed specifically for tracking victims and emergency personnel in a disaster. It was written by William Moerner, WN6I, and David Palmer, N6KL.

FBB BBS—Written by Jean-Paul Roubelat, F6FBB, this software is probably the most popular PBBS in packet radio today.

MSYS—This program is a multiple-user, multiport PBBS that supports gateway, KA-Node and TCP/IP operations. It was written by Mike Pechura, WA8BXN.

Pavilion Software Packet Conference Board System—Pavilion Software produced this packet radio conference board system for the IBM PC XT and its clones. Besides traditional message functions, including message forwarding, the system serves up to 26 users concurrently, provides multiuser conferencing, a user-to-user talk function, DX spotting announcements, DX logging and general announcement functions. For information concerning the availability of this software, write to Pavilion Software, PO Box 803, Amherst, NH 03031.

ROSErver/Packet Radio MailBox System (PRMBS)—This multiple-user PBBS/packet server attempts to eliminate some of the SYSOP maintenance that other systems require. Written by Brian Riley, KA2BQE, and Dave Trulli, NN2Z, it may be downloaded from the KB7UV ROSErver/PRMBS at 718-956-7133 (1200-9600 V.32, 8N1, don't press Enter, wait for the sign-on message) or RATS Software Server at 201-387-8898 (1200-9600 V.32, 8N1).

WØRLI Mailbox—This is the original PBBS software rewritten in C by Hank Oredson, WØRLI, and David Toth, VE3GYQ. The current version is intended for the IBM PC and its clones.

WA7MBL PBBS—This is the Jeff Jacobsen, WA7MBL, implementation of the original WØRLI PBBS for the IBM PC and its clones. It is fully compatible with WØRLI systems.

Commodore and Tandy computers fell by the wayside. The PC's only competition, Apple Macintosh, was a superior machine, but it was too expensive and, as a result, PC clones became the computer of choice of most ham shacks and the computer of choice of PBBS software authors.

Today, virtually all PBBSs are run on an IBM PC class computer with one or more TNCs and the requisite one or more sets of radio equipment (the accompanying sidebar titled "PBBS Software" details the software that is available). Some PBBS software offer functions not provided by others and the same PBBS software may offer different functions in different locales because the *system operator* or *SYSOP*, for short, may disable and enable certain functions at his or her discretion.

Although there are different types of PBBS software, their command sets are similar. Often, the more commonly used commands are the same on each system. If you know how to use one, your knowledge can be applied to any other, at least as far as performing the basic PBBS user functions.

HANDS-ON TIME-SHIFTING

As you might suspect, the basic command set that you will find in most PBBSs is based on the granddaddy of PBBS software, the *WØRLI Mailbox*. The accompanying sidebar, titled "WØRLI Mailbox Command Set," lists the commands that are available the WØRLI PBBS. The following paragraphs describe how to use these PBBS commands.

Logging On

PBBSs are plentiful, so finding one is not difficult. If an active packet-radio channel exists, it is bound to have at least one active PBBS on frequency.

Once you find a PBBS you want to use, you initiate communications with it the same way you initiate communications with other packet-radio station, that is, by connecting to it. To log on to the N4GAA-4 PBBS, for example, at the command prompt, type:

cmd: Connect N4GAA-4 <CR>

This is known as "logging on" to the PBBS and after logging on, you will receive a log-on message welcoming you and listing the PBBS's commands. For example, after you log on to PBBS N4GAA-4, it sends:

HAVEN2:K1EIC-2} Connected to BBSGAA:N4GAA-4

[FBB-5.15-AB1FHMR$]

Hello Stan.

Welcome to N4GAA BBS system

4:N4GAA (A,B,C,D,F,G,I,J,K,L,M,N,O,P,R,S,T,U,V,W,X,Y,Z,?) >

In this example, the preamble indicates the alias and call sign of the digipeater or network node (HAVEN2, K1EIC-2), if any, that was used to access the PBBS and the alias and call sign of the PBBS (BBSGAA, N4GAA-4), the PBBS software being used (FBB version 5.15), a welcome message, the PBBS's command prompt (4:N4GAA>) and a list of available commands (A,B,C,D,F,G,I,J,K,L,M,N,O,P,R,S,T,U,V,W,X,Y,Z,?).

WØRLI Mailbox Command Set

The following commands are available with the *WØRLI MailBox* public-domain PBBS software, written in "C" by Hank Oredson, WØRLI, and David Toth, VE3GYQ.

General commands

B—Log off the PBBS
J *x*—Display call signs of stations recently heard or connected on TNC port *x*
N *x*—Enter your name (*x*) in system (12 characters maximum)
NH *x*—Enter the call sign (*x*) of the PBBS where you normally send and receive mail
NQ *x*—Enter your location (*x*)
NZ *n*—Enter your ZIP Code (*n*)
P *x*—Display information concerning station whose call sign is *x*
S—Display status of PBBS
T—Ring bell at the SYSOP's terminal for one minute

Help commands

? *—Display description of all PBBS commands
?—Display summary of all PBBS commands
? *x*—Display summary of command *x*
H *—Display description of all PBBS commands
H—Display summary of all PBBS commands
H *x*—Display description of command *x*
I—Display information about PBBS
I *x*—Display information about station whose call sign is *x*
IL—Display list of local users of the PBBS
IZ *n*—List users at ZIP Code *n*
NE—Toggle between short and extended command menu
V—Display PBBS software version

Message commands

K *n*—Kill message numbered *n*
KM—Kill all messages addressed to you that you have read
KT *n*—Kill NTS traffic numbered *n*
L—List all messages entered since you last logged in
L *n*—List message numbered *n* and messages numbered higher than *n*
L< *x*—List messages from station whose call sign is *x*
L> *x*—List messages addressed to station whose call sign is *x*
L@ *x*—List messages addressed for forwarding to PBBS whose hierarchical address is *x*
L *n1 n2*—List messages numbered *n1* through *n2*
LA *n*—List the first *n* messages stored on PBBS
LB—List all bulletin messages
LF—List all messages that have been forwarded

(Continued on next page)

LL *n*—List the last *n* messages stored on PBBS
LM—List all messages addressed to you
LT—List all NTS traffic
R *n*—Read message numbered *n*
RH *n*—Read message numbered *n* with full message header displayed
RM—Read all messages addressed to you that you have not read
S *x* @ *z*—Send a message to station whose call sign is *x* at PBBS whose hierarchical address is *z*
S *x*—Send message to station whose call sign is *x*
SB *x*—Send a bulletin message to *x*
SB *x* @ *z*—Send a bulletin message to *x* at PBBS whose hierarchical address is *z*
SP *x* @ *z*—Send a private message to station whose call sign is *x* at PBBS whose hierarchical address is *z*
SP *x*—Send a private message to station whose call sign is *x*
SR—Send a message in response to a message you have just read
ST NTS *x*—Send an NTS message whose intended recipient is located in ARRL Section *x*.

File transfer commands

D *x z*—From directory named *x*, download file named *z*
U *x*—Upload file named *x*
W—List what directories are available
W*x*—List what files are available in directory named *x*
W*x z*—List files in directory named *x* whose file name matches *z*

Port commands

C *x z*—Via port *x*, send connect request to station whose call sign is *z*
C *x*—Send data via port *x*
CM *n x*—Send message numbered *n* to station whose call sign is *x*
CM *n x* @ *z*—Send message numbered *n* to station whose call sign is *x* at PBBS whose hierarchical address is *z*
M *x*—Monitor port *x*

Roundtable commands

RT—Initiate roundtable function.
<ESCape> D *x*—Allows roundtable control station to disconnect station whose call sign is *x* from roundtable
<ESCape> H—Obtain assistance
<ESCape> P—Display ports available to roundtable
<ESCape> N *x*—Enter your name (*x*)
<ESCape> Q *x*—Enter your location (*x*)
<ESCape> U—Display list of stations in roundtable

The PBBS is now ready for your command. To send a command, you simply type the letter representing the desired command along with any qualifiers related to the command, and follow your typing with a carriage return, <CR>. The carriage return causes your TNC to send the command to the PBBS. If the command is a legitimate command used in the proper way, the PBBS responds accordingly. The PBBS sends you an error message if you use an illegal command or if you use a legal command incorrectly.

Some PBBS commands consist of only one letter. For example, to request that the PBBS computer sound a bell to alert the SYSOP, you invoke a one-letter command (the letter "T" for talk to SYSOP).

Many PBBS commands use qualifiers to make the commands more specific. For example, the one-letter "L" (for list) command causes the PBBS to send you a list of all messages stored on the PBBS since the last time you logged on. If you add the qualifier "T" (for traffic) to the "L" command, the resulting "LT" command performs a more specific task. Instead of listing all of the messages stored on the PBBS since you last logged on, it lists only the messages stored on the PBBS that consist of NTS traffic. The accompanying sidebar that lists the WØRLI PBBS commands also list the command qualifiers.

When you log on to a PBBS for the first time (or after a long absence), the PBBS is likely to quiz you for information (like your name, location, etc.) for inclusion in its user database. To enter your name in the PBBS's database, use the N (for Name) command, for example, if your name is Samiam, you would type:

N Samiam <CR>

Notice that N and Samiam are separated by a space. All PBBS commands require a space between the command and any information you are sending with that command. (Note that the blank space between Samiam and <CR> is not required. It is used here for clarity.) After the log-on message and quiz, you are ready to use the PBBS.

A Directory of Messages

When you log on to a PBBS, it will inform you if there are any new messages for you (messages addressed to you that have been stored on the system since the last time you logged on). If you want to find out what other messages have been stored on the PBBS, you may obtain a directory of the stored messages by invoking the "L" (for list messages) command. Fig 9-3 illustrates a typical message directory that was produced by a PBBS after the "L" command was used.

The directory provides the following information concerning each message stored on the PBBS:

Msg#: the message number, a unique number assigned sequentially by the PBBS as each message enters the system. It is significant because you use it when you wish to read a message.

DTSL: the type and status of the message. Typical message types include B for bulletin, T for traffic, P for private, etc. For the message status, N indicates that the intended recipient of the message has not read it, Y indicates that the intended recipient has received it, F indicates that the message has been forwarded, $ indicates that the message is a bulletin.

Msg #	DTSL	Size	To	@ BBS	From	Date	Subject
44621	BX	5830	NEWS	@AMSAT	CE3BII	21-Jun	NASA News, June 14, 95
44620	B$	762	SAREX	@AMSAT	K5ARH	24-Jun	STS-71 SAREX Flight Postponed
44619	BX	3664	INFO	@AMSAT	VK6XPS	20-Jun	KSC Shuttle Status Report 16/6/95
44618	TF	729	12072	@NTSNY	AB6CP	25-Jun	QTC LOVERVILLE 12072
44617	TF	478	06484		WQ1V	25-Jun	qtc K1EIC SHELTON CT
44615	B$	855	SALE	@TRIBBS	N2JPL	24-Jun	FT 530 FOR SALE
44609	TN	588	46761	@NTSIN	N1FLO	25-Jun	1R LAGRANGE
44608	TN	565	73034	@NTSOK	N1FLO	25-Jun	1R EDMOND OK
44607	TN	517	73003	@NTSOK	N1FLO	25-Jun	1R EDMOND
44606	TN	482	43230	@NTSOH	N1FLO	25-Jun	1R GAHONNA
44605	TF	480	43230	@NTSOH	N1FLO	25-Jun	1R GAHONNA
44604	TN	543	20904	@NTSMD	N1FLO	24-Jun	1R SILVER SPRINGS
44602	TF	273	K1EIC		W1NRG	25-Jun	Field Day Report
44593	TN	319	NI1U		NM1K	25-Jun	qtc
44575	TF	492	01036	@NTSMA	WB2SMT	24-Jun	QTC: HAMPDEN 413-566
44574	TF	514	06053		WB2SMT	24-Jun	QTC: NEW BRITAIN 203-225
44567	B$	4179	KEPS	@AMSAT	K5ARH	23-Jun	Orbital Elements 174.MICROS
44566	B$	2266	KEPS	@AMSAT	N2IXL	23-Jun	Orbital Elements 174.MISC
44563	BX	2290	HUMOR	@USBBS	KB3BBG	18-Jun	SPORTS HUMOR 001
44562	BX	1818	HUMOR	@USBBS	KB3BBG	18-Jun	Humor in the classroom
44561	BX	1041	ALL	@USBBS	N3JBG	18-Jun	WANTED OPINIONS ON ICOM 706
44560	BX	1331	CQ	@USBBS	KD6TBE	21-Jun	CQ50 ENDORCEMENTS

Fig 9-3—A PBBS's response to the "L" command.

Size: the size of the message indicates the number of bytes that the message contains. This may help you decide to read or skip a message. For example, if a message is long, you may not wish to read it during the hours of high activity.

To: the intended recipient of the message.

@ BBS: the intended destination PBBS of the message, if any.

The intended audience of the message and the "home" PBBS of its intended audience indicate how the originator of the message addressed it. These are also useful in deciding whether or not to read a message. You probably would have no interest in reading a message addressed to another individual other then yourself, however, if you are a satellite aficionado, you may be interested in reading a message addressed to ALL@AMSAT or if you use a Commodore Amiga computer, you may be interested in reading a message addressed to ALL@AMIGA. You will soon discover that the addresses of some messages are too general (ALL@ALLOVER) to be of much use. As a result, you will have to refer to the Title of the message to decide to read or skip a message.

From: the station that originated the message.

Date: the date (in day-month format) that the message was originated.

Title: the subject of the message.

The problem with the L command is that it is too general. When you invoke it, the PBBS flushes its directory and presents you with screen after screen of message listings that can quickly lose you in its wake. As the message listings scroll by, you get the feeling you are aboard a runaway train!

Luckily, the L command can be modified to provide a more discriminating and manageable directory of messages. In order to modify the L, you simply add the proper qualifier(s) to the command and, the mod is complete! For example, if you are interested in viewing a directory of bulletin messages only, add the letter B to the L command and it becomes the LB (list bulletins) command. If your interest in bulletins is narrower, you can view a directory of only those bulletin messages that have been originated "locally," that is, at the PBBS you are using. To do this, add the at-sign to the L command and you have the L@ (list local bulletins) command.

There are also some useful modified L commands for those of you who are interested only in your own messages. There is the LM (list mine) command, which only deals with commands addressed to you. Some PBBSs, like FBB, allow you to be more specific. The LU (list unread) command allows you to view a directory of those messages addressed to *and* from you that have not been read, that is, they are still new to you or to the station you addressed them to. You can be even more specific and use the LN (list new) command to view a directory of those messages addressed only to you that you have not read (those that are still new to you).

You can use numbers to modify the L command, too. For example, to list a range of messages between any two numbers, say 700 and 735, you invoke the L command followed by a space and the range of message numbers separated by a hyphen (L 700-735). Another example, to list all the messages with message numbers that are higher than a particular message number, you invoke the L command followed by that number (for example, L 1234 will list all messages numbered higher than 1234). A variation on the numbers theme is the LL (list last) command. Invoke the LL command followed by a particular number (LL *n*) and the PBBS will list the last *n* messages that have been stored on the PBBS (for example, LL 12 lists the last 12 messages stored). If you do not specify a number, LL will list the last 10 messages stored on the system.

You may also limit directory listings to certain fields that are displayed in a directory listing, that is, the to, from and @ fields. To list messages addressed to a particular station, use the L> command followed by a space and the call sign of that station (for example, L> WA1LOU lists only messages addressed to WA1LOU). On the other hand, to list messages originated from a particular station, you use the L< command followed by a space and the call sign of that station (for example, L< WA1LOU lists only messages originated from WA1LOU). If you only wish to list messages addressed to a particular PBBS, use the L@ command followed by a space and the call sign of the PBBS (for example, L@ N4GAA lists messages addressed to PBBS N4GAA).

All the L commands I have described list messages starting with the newest message (the message most recently stored on the PBBS) and scrolling to the oldest one. Some PBBSs allow you to list the messages starting with the oldest one and working your way up to the newest one, use the LR (list reverse) command. Note that the LR command often may be modified like the L command. For example, to list a range of messages, say between 700 and 735, invoke the LR command followed by a space and the range of message numbers separated by a hyphen (LR 700-735).

If, after you invoke a L - List command, things start to get out of hand, you can order the PBBS to cease and desist by invoking the A (abort) command. This command is not supported by all PBBSs, but where it is supported, it will cause the PBBS to stop sending you its directory of messages. When you use the A command, do not get anxious when the directory listing does not stop immediately. What is happening is that while the A command is heading to the PBBS, the PBBS is sending more directory listings your way. No matter how close the PBBS is to your station, there is liable to be some directory listings in transit to you before the PBBS will receive and react to your A command. So, be a little patient after you issue the A command; your reward is not far behind.

Reading the Mail

Once you have determined that there are messages stored on the PBBS that you are interested in reading, you may use the "RM" (for read mine) command to read only those messages addressed to you. You may also use the "R" (for read message) command followed by the message's number to read a particular message. In either case, after you invoke the command, the PBBS retrieves the requested message from its storage and sends it to you for your reading pleasure.

The *message header* is displayed before the actual contents of the requested message. Usually, the message header contains some of the same information concerning the message that is displayed when you invoke the L command. The header contains the call sign of its originator, its intended recipient, type, status, etc. If the message has been forwarded from one or more other PBBSs, the call sign of each PBBS that has relayed the message is listed under the "Path:" portion of the header. An example of the header of a forwarded message follows.

From : K5ARH

To : SAREX @AMSAT

Type/status : B$

Date/time : 24-Jun 22:27

Bid : STS-71.001

Message # : 44620

Title : STS-71 SAREX Flight Postponed

Path: !N2BQF!WA2AWG!K5ARH!

In this example, the Path information indicates that the message was originated at PBBS K5ARH and relayed through PBBSs WA2AWG and N2BQF before it arrived at PBBS N4GAA-4.

The text of the message is displayed after the header. When you have read any messages that are addressed only to you, you should delete them to free some space in the PBBS's storage. You can delete a specific message by invoking the "K" (for kill message) command followed by the number of the message you wish to delete. For example, to delete message number 3773, type:

K 3773 <CR>

Qualifiers may also be used with the K command. The most commonly used K command qualifier is "M" (for mine). The resulting "KM" (for kill mine) command deletes all messages addressed to you that you have already read.

Post Office of the Air

Sending a message through a PBBS is similar to sending a message through a postal system: you compose a message, address it and send it on its way. The key to successful delivery is proper addressing. If you wrote a message to me and stuck it in an envelope with my name and the proper postage attached, it is unlikely I would receive it. However, if you added "One Glen Avenue, Downtown Wolcott, CT 06716-1442" to the envelope, I would probably receive your message a day or two after you sent it.

Similarly, if you wrote a packet message to me with only my call sign in the address, chances are I would not receive it. However, if you added @N4GAA.CT.USA.NOAM to my call sign, I would likely receive it in a day or two after you sent it. Just as a postal system message must be addressed with my name and where I receive my mail, that is, my home, packet messages must be addressed with my call sign and where I receive my packet mail, my home PBBS.

The postal and packet mailing systems only require that you know the intended destination of the message. You do not have to be concerned with the intermediary post offices or packet stations that may have to relay the message. Your local post office and PBBS know where to relay your message so that I will receive it in Downtown Wolcott. It is not your concern.

I don't know what the postal system calls it (maybe "dumb luck"), but in the packet system, it is called "automatic forwarding" or "auto-forwarding" for short. When you hand over your message to the local PBBS, it automatically consults a table to look up where it has to relay your message so that it gets to N4GAA.CT.USA.NOAM (the local PBBS for Downtown Wolcott). With that information, it will eventually connect with that relay station and send your message. That station does an automatic look up to pass your message to the next station down the line. This process is repeated until your message reaches N4GAA.

Sending Mail

Sending mail by means of a PBBS is accomplished by using the "S" (for send message) command. Simply invoke the S command followed by the intended recipient of your message. If the intended recipient is another Amateur Radio operator, you type the letter S followed by the ham's call sign, for example:

S K1EIC <CR>

The intended recipient does not have to be an individual Amateur Radio operator. For example, you can address the message to "ALL" in cases where your message contains information of general interest. You can also address the message to a specific group (to "YLS," for example).

If you are sending the message to a ham at another PBBS, your message must be automatically forwarded to the other PBBS. In this case, you use the S command followed by the call sign of the intended recipient, the at-sign (@), the call sign of the destination PBBS and its location. For example, to send a message to K1EIC at PBBS N4GAA, you type:

S K1EIC @ N4GAA.CT.USA.NOAM <CR>

The *hierarchical address* of the message's address (N4GAA.CT.USA.NOAM) is intended to help the network forward the message to its intended destination in cases where the PBBS's location is unknown. In this example, if the network did not know the location of N4GAA, it would still point the message in the right direction because the continent field of the hierarchical address (NOAM) indicates that N4GAA is located in North America, the country field of the hierarchical address (USA) indicates that N4GAA is located in the United States and the region field of the hierarchical address (CT) indicates that N4GAA is located in Connecticut.

All messages intended for PBBSs in the United States use the two-letter postal abbreviation for the destination PBBS's state in the region field of the address followed by .USA.NOAM. Messages intended for PBBSs in Canada use the two-letter postal abbreviation for the destination PBBS's province in the region field of the address followed by .CAN.NOAM. Messages intended for other countries require appropriate abbreviations in the hierarchical address fields, for example, messages intended for PBBS SPØBBS in Poland would have a hierarchical address of SP0BBS.POL.EURO.

In some regions, more specific geographic information is added to the hierarchical address. These more specific designations are only recognized by systems within the region using them, so a number sign (#) is placed in front of these designations so out-of-state systems will ignore them. For example, some day the PBBS operators in Connecticut may decide that more specific designations are needed and that mail heading into Downtown Wolcott should use the #DTWL designation. Thus, the address WA1LOU@N4GAA.CT.USA.NOAM would become WA1LOU@N4GAA.#DTWL.CT.USA.NOAM .

The PBBS can handle private messages (messages that are not intended for general consumption). To send a private message, use the SP (for send private) command followed by the call sign of the intended recipient of the message. After a private message is stored on a PBBS, only the station that sent the private message and the intended recipient of the private message (or the SYSOP) can list, read, or kill the message. The SP command also relieves other users from having to see mail listed that they have no interest (or permission) to read.

If you wish to send a message to the general public, use the SB (for send bulletin) command. Instead of addressing your message to a particular call sign, you must tailor the address for its intended audience. For example, if your intended audience is all the users of the N4GAA PBBS, the bulletin's address would be ALL@N4GAA. A bulletin intended for NOS users of all the PBBSs in Oregon would be addressed to NOS@ORBBS. An announcement about a hamfest in Podunk would be addressed to HAMFST@PODUNK.

After you address the message, the PBBS will prompt you for a title for your message. If you are sending a message to another person, the subject is not critical, however, if you are generating a bulletin, your subject should be informative because, in 30 characters or less, you are trying to entice people to read your message. End the title with a <CR> and the PBBS will now prompt you to send your message. You may type your message manually or you may upload the message from RAM or disk storage, if your terminal or computer has the capability. In either case, keep your message as short as possible. More and more mail is being transferred around the globe each day, so economizing your words will lighten the load. Also be sure to insert a <CR> at the end of each line of your message (each line should be less than 80 characters in length including spaces). The line-ending <CR>s are required because some systems can only handle lines of a finite length. Lines that are too long get truncated.

After the contents of your message is sent to the PBBS, type <CTRL-Z> <CR> or the character sequence of /EX <CR> to indicate to the PBBS that the end of the message has been sent. When the PBBS receives the <CTRL-Z> or /EX, it stores your message for later retrieval or for mail forwarding.

To speed up the process of sending a message, you can create it off line with a word processor or text editor using the following format:

name/call sign of recipient @ PBBS, if any <CR>
title of message <CR>
line 1 of message text <CR>
line 2 of message text <CR>
line 3 of message text <CR>
...
...
last line of message text <CR>
<CTRL-Z> <CR>

You supply the information in italics, then save it all in the ASCII format under an appropriate file name (perhaps, the call sign of the intended recipient).

When you log on to your local PBBS, send the file and it will be interpreted as another message being sent using the S command (for private messages, use "SP" instead of "S" in the first line of the file). The PBBS will still prompt you for the title and text of your message. These prompts should be ignored because that information has already been sent in your file. (The reason you see these prompts is that when the PBBS detects the "S" command in the first line of the file, it sends you a message title prompt before it reads the second line of your file. Similarly, when the PBBS reads the title of your message in the second line of your file, it sends you a message text prompt before it reads the third line of your file.)

File Manipulation

Most PBBSs have files stored in their computer system. These files may consist of digipeater, network and PBBS maps, packet-radio news, public-domain software, Amateur Radio newsletters, or almost anything of interest to the amateur packet radio operator.

To find out what files are stored on a PBBS, use the "W" (for what files) command. Often, the PBBS's file storage is subdivided into two or more subdirectories. If this is the case, the PBBS will respond to the W command by asking you to be more specific and to append a qualifier to the W command. For example, your local PBBS may have four subdirectories named "A" through "D." To find out what is stored under subdirectory "C," you type:

WC <CR>

The PBBS responds by sending you a list of the names of all the files stored under subdirectory C. The "W" command also shows how much free space is available for new files on the PBBS disk(s).

If you wish to receive a file from the PBBS, that is, *download* a file, you use the "D" (for download file) command, followed by the name of the desired file. The name of the file you request must be entered exactly as it appeared when you invoked the W command. The PBBS will not be able to find the file if you do not specify the name correctly. If the file is stored in a subdirectory, the subdirectory qualifier must be appended to the D command.

Some PBBSs require slightly different formats when you use the D command with a subdirectory qualifier. For example, some PBBSs (like WØRLI) require that the D command be immediately followed by the subdirectory qualifier, a space, and the file name. Some other PBBSs (like WA7MBL) require that the D command be followed by a space, the subdirectory qualifier, a slash (/), and the file name. For example, using a PBBS like WØRLI to download a file named *TNC.DOC* from subdirectory "B," you type:

DB *TNC.DOC* <CR>

Using a PBBS like WA7MBL to download a file named *NOCA.MAP* from subdirectory "MAPS," you type:

D MAPS/*NOCA.MAP* <CR>

The PBBS responds to your use of the D command by finding the requested file and sending it to you. (If your terminal is actually a computer emulating a terminal, you may be able to save the received file to disk for later reading, printing or uploading. If this is the case and you wish to save the file, you should enable the terminal's file-save function when you invoke the D command.)

If you wish to store a file at the PBBS, (upload a file), you use the "U" (for upload file) command. If subdirectories exist on the PBBS, the U command requires the same subdirectory qualifier as the D command (with the same differences between the WØRLI and WA7MBL systems).

Most PBBSs you will encounter are being run on an IBM-PC/MS-DOS class computer and, as a result, the file names on a PBBS usually adhere to the naming conventions of IBM-PC/MS-DOS. According to this convention, a file name may consist of one to eight characters and optionally may be followed by an extension consisting of a period and one to three characters (typically, three characters), for example, *FILENAME* and *FILENAME.TXT*, but not *FILESNAMED* or *FILENAME.TEXT*. The files you upload must follow these naming conventions unless you are directed differently. Note that file extensions typically help to identify the file, for example, the extension .TXT identifies the file as an ASCII/text file, .BAS identifies the file as a BASIC computer language program, etc.

When you upload a file, you should use terminal software that automates the process. In theory, you can enter a file into PBBS storage by typing the file manually at your computer's keyboard, however, this is very inefficient. In practice, manual typing is bound to contain errors and is undoubtedly very time consuming. Instead, you should prepare the file beforehand using a word processor and saving the file in ASCII/text format in the computer's RAM or, preferably, on something more permanent like a computer disk. Then you should use a terminal program that, on command, reads the file from storage and sends it over the air to the PBBS (after you invoke the U command).

When the file transfer is complete, send the PBBS a <CTRL-Z> and a <CR> to inform the system that the end of the file has been sent. When the PBBS receives this end-of-file indication, it closes and stores the file.

You do not want to be informed that you have used up all the available storage space in the middle of a file transfer. Unless the "W" command shows that there is plenty of disk space available, you should ask the PBBS SYSOP if there is enough storage space available for your file before you upload it. Use the "T" (for talk to SYSOP) command to elicit an immediate response (if the SYSOP is available) or use the S command to send the SYSOP a message. Also, if the file you are uploading or downloading is a long one, you might consider performing the file transfer off hours, that is, when the PBBS is less active to minimize the effect your transfer will have on other users.

PBBS Assistance

A number of PBBS commands provide assistance to users in the form of specific information that can be provided by the PBBS on request. Two commands that provide general assistance are the "H" (for help) command, which provides a short description of each PBBS command, and the "I" (for information) command, which provides a short description of the PBBS itself. The N4GAA-4 PBBS's response to the I command is typical:

N4GAA Nodes, BBSGAA and IPGAA descriptions :

BBSGAA

-Qth : West Haven, CT.

-Computer : 486 DX 66 MHz clone, 8 MB RAM, 200 MB hard disk.

-Software : FBB Release 515B. Multiconnect and multilingual.

-4 ports and 20 channels :

Port	SYSTEM	Name	Frequency	Tx	Antenna
1	HF	20MTS	20 Meters	Kenwood 940	Beam
2	HF	30MTS	30 Meters	Icom 720a	Dipole
3	Phone	14,400 Hayes Modem			Ask for access
4	20 VHF/UHF	All Netrom Nodes			

Node Stack here at N4GAA

Port	Node Call	Frequency	Radio	Antenna
1	N4GAA-2	145.09	Yaesu 270r	Vertical
2	BACKBONE	22X.XXX	Yaesu 311rm	Vertical
3	N4GAA-7	441.05	Icom 3200	Vertical
4	N4GAA-8	IPGAA	TCP/IP	Gateway Diode Matrix
5	N4GAA-10	QSO1	International Chat node	

TCP/IP System

Enjoy the system

73 Jay N4GAA

The J (for just heard or just connected) command assists the user by providing information concerning packet radio activity and how to get at it. The J command lists the call signs of the stations most recently heard by the PBBS or the call signs of the stations most recently connected to the PBBS. Qualifiers to the J command expand its usefulness. For example, the J command followed by the qualifier "A" (for the TNC connected to the PBBS's port A), lists the call signs of the stations most recently heard by and connected to the TNC on the PBBS's port A with the monitored time and date noted. Whereas, the J command followed by the qualifier "L" (for list connected stations), lists only the call signs of the stations most recently connected to the PBBS with the monitored time and date noted.

Finally, there is the "T" (for talk to SYSOP) command that allows you to obtain information right from the horse's mouth. When you send the T command, the bell at the SYSOP's terminal rings for one minute to get the SYSOP's attention. If the SYSOP responds, you may converse with him directly. If the SYSOP does not respond, you will be informed of that fact and be offered an alternative, such as, "SYSOP did not answer, you might leave a message in the Mailbox."

Logging Off

When you are finished using a PBBS, you must *log off* to inform the PBBS that you are finished using it. This can be done by switching your TNC to the Command Mode (by entering <CTRL-C>) and invoking the Disconnect command, but the preferred way to log off is to send the B (for bye) command to the PBBS. Bye is preferred because it allows the PBBS to perform internal housework concerning your PBBS session and then disconnect cleanly. It also saves you the trouble of transferring to the command mode in order to disconnect.

If the system does not receive a packet from you within a few minutes, the PBBS automatically logs you off and disconnects. This automatic disconnect function prevents the PBBS from being tied up if conditions have deteriorated and your packets can no longer be received or if you simply forget to log off a connected PBBS.

TRAFFIC HANDLING

As far back as 1984, packet radio was being used to handle National Traffic System (NTS) traffic. At that time, NTS traffic was stored on various PBBSs in standard ARRL radiogram format along with other PBBS messages. Since the packet radio network was not as extensive then as it is today, an operator could never be sure that the traffic would be forwarded and delivered to its intended destination. Back then, it was often recommended that a prayer be recited after an NTS message was stored on a PBBS.

Today, if you store a properly addressed message on a PBBS, there is an excellent chance that it will reach its intended destination in a very short time. There are a number of reasons for this improvement in message handling. The packet radio network is much more organized today, and it reaches into every populated nook and cranny of the United States and Canada. The major PBBS programs in use support NTS message handling. The NTS has become more packet radio oriented, while packet radio has become more NTS oriented.

Handling Traffic via a PBBS

The typical PBBS has commands that support NTS message handling and the packet radio-based NTS traffic auto-forwarding network has simplified the forwarding of NTS traffic to its intended destination.

Sending NTS traffic via packet radio is easy. First, log on to your local PBBS and invoke the ST (send traffic) command as follows:

ST *XXXXX* @*NTSYY*

where *XXXXX* is the ZIP Code and *YY* the 2-letter abbreviation for the state/province where the intended recipient of the traffic resides.

After you invoke the ST command, the PBBS will prompt you for a subject. To facilitate the delivery of the traffic, enter "QTC 1" followed by the addressee's town or city and, optionally, telephone area code and local exchange (separated by a hyphen), for example, QTC 1 Wolcott 203-879.

After you enter the title, the PBBS will prompt you for the text of the message. The text should be sent in standard ARRL radiogram format with a message number, precedence, handling instructions (optional), call sign of the station of origin, check, place of origin, time of filing (optional) and date, followed by the name, address, and telephone number of the intended recipient of the message. The actual text of the message comes next, followed by the signature. (If precedence or check is Greek to you, please refer to any ARRL publication that deals with traffic handling. For example, *The ARRL Operating Manual* is a good source for basic traffic-handling information.) When you are finished entering the message, send a <CTRL-Z> and <CR> to the PBBS and it will store the message for forwarding through the packet radio network to its intended destination.

After a message is forwarded to a PBBS, how does it get transferred from the PBBS to its ultimate destination? Another operator at the destination end must take the traffic from the PBBS and deliver it, or relay it to a section or local NTS net for delivery.

If you wish to handle traffic, log on to your local PBBS and invoke the LT (list traffic) command. The PBBS will respond with a directory of all of the NTS traffic stored on the PBBS. Scan the titles of the listed messages to find any that you can handle (by relaying the message to an NTS local or section net or by delivering the message to its intended recipient via a telephone call). If you can handle a message, use the R (read) or RT (read traffic) command followed by the message's number to receive a copy of the message. It's a good idea to use some kind of hard-copy device at this point; either send the message directly to a printer as the PBBS sends it to you or save it to a file for printing at a later time. After you obtain a copy of the message, use the KT (kill traffic) command followed by the received message's number to remove the message from the PBBS. The message is now in your hands for telephone delivery or further NTS relay.

GOOD OPERATING PROCEDURES

PBBS operations are very popular. When you use a PBBS, there are likely to be other stations waiting in line to use the PBBS as soon as you are through. For this reason, you should be sure that you use the system in the most time-efficient manner. By following a few simple PBBS operating procedures, you will be able to log on to the PBBS, check the latest messages and log off as quickly as possible.

Patience is a virtue whenever you send a command to the PBBS. Most of the time the PBBS responds quickly, but sometimes the response may be delayed. Delays are usually caused by packet collisions during high levels of channel activity. Whatever the cause, if the PBBS does not respond to your command quickly, be patient and do not send the command again. If the link between your station and the PBBS is any good and you repeat a command, the PBBS will eventually receive the command twice. Since the PBBS is only a computer, it will respond to the command twice. If the response to a repeated command is time consuming, that time is now doubled! When you send a command, once is enough.

If you are going to send more than one command to the PBBS, you can save time by sending more than one command at one time. Since each PBBS command must be followed by a <CR>, it would seem impossible to send more than one command because that same <CR> also forces the TNC to send a packet. There is a way around this: the <CR> must be disguised so that the TNC does not recognize it as the Sendpac (send packet) character. This is accomplished by using the "Pass" character, which causes the TNC to ignore whatever character immediately follows it (by default, the pass character is <CTRL-V>). Whenever you want the TNC to ignore a <CR>, precede the <CR> with a <CTRL-V>. For example, to send the L, RM, KM, and J commands in one packet, you would type:

L <CTRL-V> <CR> RM <CTRL-V> <CR> KM <CTRL-V> <CR> J <CR>

In order to send this packet, the TNC must recognize a <CR> at the end of the string of commands, so a <CTRL-V> must not precede the final <CR> in the string.

Do not perform time-consuming tasks during the prime-time operating periods. Prime time is not the time to upload or download long files or to list all of the messages stored on the system. During prime time, the level of activity is high and the resulting packet collisions cause the time-consuming tasks to consume even more time. Other stations are probably waiting to use the PBBS, so save the time-consuming tasks for later.

Finally, all PBBSs do not support all PBBS commands. Some of the commands I have described may not be supported by your PBBS. When you issue a particular command, it may do something unexpected or do nothing at all and send you an error message. On the other hand, the functions of the commands I have described may be supported on your PBBS, but those function may require you to invoke a different command than the one I described. When in doubt, use the Help functions of your PBBS for assistance.

RUNNING YOUR OWN PBBS

After they get a taste of PBBS operations, many amateurs get the urge to place their own system on the air. Monitoring the packet radio channels shows clear evidence of this as more and more PBBS operations appear on the air every day. As many new PBBSs appear, many also disappear. The reason for this is that running a PBBS requires more time and effort than many operators realize at first.

To understand this better, let's look at what it takes to run a PBBS. For starters, consider the outlay of equipment that must be dedicated to the cause. To run a PBBS requires a complete packet radio station (TNC, radio and antenna) and a computer to run the PBBS software. Unless you plan to run your PBBS on a part-time basis, you must dedicate this equipment to PBBS operation full time. (A part-time PBBS seems to be a good solution, but it's really not because the time you are likely to want to use your equipment is the same time that others are likely to want to use your PBBS.)

Besides dedicating some equipment, running a PBBS requires dedicating some of your free time. A PBBS does not run without maintenance. Besides maintaining equipment, the operator must maintain the PBBS software. Depending on the software and the amount of usage that your PBBS experiences, there are chores that must be performed in order to keep the software running properly.

If you believe that you have enough dedication to run a PBBS, the next step is to decide where to put your PBBS: HF, VHF or UHF? In many areas, PBBSs proliferate on 2 meters. If there is a 2-meter PBBS next door, why put another PBBS on that band? Why not choose a packet-radio channel that has a need for a PBBS? Besides 2 meters, the other VHF and UHF bands are good choices. The Novice 220-MHz band is prime area for a PBBS. Or how about a PBBS on 6 or 15 meters, where there are very few PBBS operations? With the sunspot cycle swinging favorably towards those bands, 6 and 15-meter PBBSs will be very much in demand. Note that if you plan on putting a PBBS on any VHF or UHF band, you should contact your area frequency coordinator (as listed in the *ARRL Repeater Directory*) and find out what requirements, if any, exist for PBBS operations. There may be a plan in effect that confines PBBS operations to certain frequencies. Better to check first, and avoid being sorry later.

After you determine where your PBBS will operate, you must obtain the required equipment. Radio equipment (transmitter, receiver, antenna and peripherals) for the selected frequency must be procured. A TNC is a necessity. A computer must be selected to run the PBBS software. Unless you plan to write your own PBBS software, make sure that the computer you select is a PC or clone.

Finally, you must obtain the PBBS software (refer to the sidebar titled "PBBS Software" for sources). The software's documentation will describe how to set up the PBBS equipment. The selection of certain TNC parameters is critical for PBBS operation, so make sure that you check the documentation for the specifics.

Running a PBBS requires a lot of dedication, but it is also a satisfying experience because you are providing a service to others. The bottom line is that it is also a lot of fun.

CONCLUSION

For ages, man has been intrigued by the possibility of controlling time. With PBBS and mailbox operation, hams have achieved time control on a limited basis.

10

DX Packet Clusters

Finding new DX or contest multiplier stations and announcing their presence over the air is nothing new. During the 1970s and 1980s, FM repeaters were used to announce the presence of stations that may represent a new country or contest multiplier to those stations monitoring the repeater. Such systems have been successful in cranking up DXCC totals and contest scores and many serious DX and contest clubs employ such systems. However, the FM repeater spotting system had some problems.

One problem is that spot announcements can be distracting while you are intently working another station. Typically, if a spot announcement blasted through in the middle of a contact, you quickly turned off the FM radio and attempted to complete your contact without the distraction. Maybe you remembered to turn the FM radio back on after the contact was completed and maybe you didn't. Another reason to turn off the FM radio (and forget to turn it back on) was that unless the repeater was dedicated to spotting operation, there was liable to be other non-spotting activity on the repeater to further distract you. In either case, while the FM radio was off, you knew Murphy would strike and you'd miss an announcement for a new country or multiplier!

There were other problems, too. What you heard was not necessarily what was said. As a result, instead of chasing a new multiplier on 14.103, you ended up chasing air on 14.301. Also, all spot announcements were not important to you, yet you still had to listen to them all. If you were working a single band, announcements concerning activity on other bands were useless. Finally, by their nature, FM repeater coverage was limited and the club repeater may not have encompassed all of the territory where the club's members lived.

Although spot announcements via FM repeaters were often helpful, things could be better. New advances in packet radio solved many of the problems that were inherent to spot announcements via FM repeaters.

PACKETCLUSTER: PACKET CONFERENCE SOFTWARE

Normally, one packet radio station may only communicate with one other packet radio station at any one time. Now, conference software is available for installation at key packet radio stations or nodes to permit other packet radio stations to communicate with more than one station at a time. When a station is connected to a conference node, it is able to communicate with all of the other stations connected to the same conference.

Software is also available to link conference nodes together so a station connected to one conference node can communicate with stations connected to other conference nodes. The combination of conference software and node-to-node linking software can result in an enhanced DX and contest club spotting network that covers all of the members of the club, and beyond.

Pavillion Software's *PacketCluster* software allows conference nodes to be linked together and provides PBBS operation with multiple-user capability. Up to 104 stations may be connected to the system concurrently and these stations may remain connected to the system and in constant communication with each other.

PacketCluster provides functions that are specifically designed for spotting announcements. If you hear or work a station that may be of interest to other stations on the cluster, you can connect with the local *PacketCluster* node and use the DX command to make a spot announcement ("Dx 1S1DX 14.152 LISTENING UP 5," for example) and your announcement is displayed at the terminal of every station connected to the system. There is no chance of misinterpretation because the announcement is printed clearly for all to read and there is no chance of missing an announcement because a bell will sound at each terminal whenever an announcement is made. On the other hand, if a user has disabled the bell (SEt/NOBEep), each announcement will be printed silently for reading at the monitoring station's pleasure. And, if the announcement scrolls off the display, it is not lost forever because the system logs the announcement for review later.

Perhaps, the most powerful command in the *PacketCluster* command set is the Show command. For example, the Show DX command (SHow/DX) displays the last five DX announcements including the DX station's operating frequency, call sign, the date and time of the announcement, other pertinent information concerning the DX station (long path, LOUD, weak and so on) and the call sign of the station that made the announcement. Appending a number to the Show DX command (SHow/DX/10) displays that number of previous DX announcements. If you are operating a single band and are not interested in activity on other bands, you can invoke the Show DX command followed by a specific band (SHow/DX 21) and the last five DX announcements on the specified band are displayed. Or specify how many DX announcements for a specified band you want to see and that will show up on your terminal, too (see Fig 10-1).

When V51NAM is at the bottom of a pileup on 20 meters, you can use the cluster to get some ammunition before you try to work him. Assuming you have already en-

```
WA1LOU de KB1H    28-Mar 0021Z >
SH/DX/15 50

 50139.8  KW0F?      28-Mar-1995 0020Z  EM19>FN65 WEAK                 <VE9AA>
 50130.3  WR0G       28-Mar-1995 0015Z  EN31 LOUD!!                    <N3QYA>
 50137.8  N7ML       28-Mar-1995 0013Z  mike,montana>fn31,not here     <VE9AA>
 50137.9  WZ1V       28-Mar-1995 0012Z  fn31>fn65 short!               <VE9AA>
 50125.0  W2/W3S     28-Mar-1995 0008Z  as close as fn31, 2m Es?       <VE9AA>
 50145.1  VE1KCO     27-Mar-1995 2359Z                             <WB4DBB-6>
 50175.0  VE1PZ      27-Mar-1995 2349Z  call corr                      <N3QYA>
 50175.0  VE1AZ      27-Mar-1995 2349Z  >fm18                         <WA3SEE>
 50110.0  VP9MZ      27-Mar-1995 2346Z  cw                             <W2CAP>
 50105.3  FP5EK      27-Mar-1995 2338Z  WRKD FOR # 100 ON 6.       <WB4DBB-6>
 50130.0  VP9MZ      27-Mar-1995 2337Z  CW broke in QSO                 <KM1H>
 50105.2  FP5EK      27-Mar-1995 2323Z  gn16 CQing CW                   <K3DI>
 50105.0  FP5EK      27-Mar-1995 2310Z  CW GN16 > FN30                  <K2MT>
 50105.0  FP5EK      27-Mar-1995 2310Z  >FN20                          <W3IWU>
 50110.5  CU1CB      27-Mar-1995 2308Z  CW band wont quit!!!            <KM1H>
WA1LOU de KB1H    28-Mar 0021Z >
```

Fig 10-1—WA1LOU enters "SH/DX/15 50" to command *PacketCluster* node KB1H to display the last 15 DX spot announcements for 6 meters. The resulting display indicates the operating frequency, call sign, date and time of each spot, as well as comments, if any, concerning the spot and the call sign of the station making the spot.

tered your radio shack's longitude and latitude in the cluster's database using the Set Location command (SEt/LOCATion), invoke the Show Heading command for Namibia (SHow/Heading V51). The cluster will perform some calculations and send results that will look something like this:

V51 Namibia: 107 degs

Q dist: 7238 mi, 11649 km

Reciprocal heading: 309 degs

Now you can use the Show Sun command (SHow/SUn V51) and the cluster will respond with:

V51 Namibia Sunrise: 0455Z Sunset: 1703Z

The Show Sun command is also handy for finding out your local sunrise and sunset. Simply invoke the command without appending a prefix (SHow/SUn) and the cluster will send:

<your call> QTH Q Sunrise: 1055Z Sunset: 2303Z

Finally, try using the Show MUF command (SHow/Muf V51) and the cluster will respond:

Namibia propagation: MUF: 22.7 MHz LUF: 2.3 MHz

Other variations of the Show command include the Show WWV command (SHow/

Wwv) to obtain WWV propagation information and the Show Users (SHow/Users) command to obtain a list of all the other stations connected to the cluster. The Show command also may access any database installed on your local packet-cluster. Such databases may include the contest or DX club membership rosters, contest information, DX news, FCC rules and regulations, IRC data, QSL bureau addresses, etc.

Another function of *PacketCluster* is its bulletin board system that operates in a fashion similar to a standard PBBS. Like other PBBSs, the *PacketCluster* system tells you when you have new mail. To read mail, or any message or bulletin, you use the Read command. To post a message or bulletin of your own, you use the Send command. To obtain a list of the messages and bulletins that are on the board, you use the Directory or List command, and to remove a message or bulletin from the board, you use the Delete or Kill command. The *PacketCluster* can even be set up to automatically do mail-forwarding to PBBSs beyond the cluster. (The sidebar titled "DX *PacketCluster* Command Set" describes all of the packet-cluster commands.)

As you can see, the *PacketCluster* is a powerful tool. Although similar tools existed in the past, only packet radio could make it as powerful as it is today. Faster packets will only make it more powerful in the future.

DX *PacketCluster* Command Set

The following commands are available with Pavillion Software's DX *PacketCluster* software. The uppercase portion of each command name is the shorthand version of the command; the lowercase portion is optional. For example, entering "D" or "Directory" will perform the same function.

Announce *m*—Send message *m* to all stations connected to the local node.

Announce/Full *m*—Send message *m* to all stations connected to the cluster.

Announce/Sysop—Send message *m* to Sysop(s) of cluster.

Announce/*x m*—Send message *m* to station on the cluster whose call sign is *x*.

Announce/*x m*—Send message *m* to stations on distribution list *x*.

Bye—Disconnect from cluster.

CONFERence—Enter the conference mode on the local node.

CONFERence/Full—Enter the conference mode on the cluster.

DElete—Delete last message you read.

DElete *n*—Delete message numbered *n*.

DIrectory—List active messages on local node.

DIrectory/All—List all active messages on local node.

DIrectory/Bulletin—List active messages addressed to "all."

DIrectory/*n*—List the specified number (*n*) of most recent active messages.

DIrectory/New—List active messages added since you last invoked the DIrectory command.

DIrectory/Own—List active messages addressed from or to you.

DIrectory/Subject *x*—List active messages with *x* in their title.

Dx *x z a*—Announce DX station whose call sign is *x* on frequency *z* followed by comment *a*, for example, Dx SP1N 14.205 up 2.

Dx/*b x z a*—Announce DX station whose call sign is *x* on frequency *z* followed by comment *a* with credit given to station whose call sign is *b*, for example, Dx/K1CC SP1N 14.205 up 2.

EXECUTE—Run your personal command procedure.

Findfile *x*—Find file named *x*.

Help or ?—Display a summary of all commands.

Help *x*—Display help for command *x*.

Kill—Delete last message you read.

Kill *n*—Delete message numbered *n*.

List—List active messages on local node.

List/All—List all active messages on local node.

List/Bulletin—List active messages addressed to "all."

List/*n*—List the *n* most recent active messages.

List/New—List active messages added since you last invoked the List command.

(Continued on next page)

List/Own—List active messages addressed from or to you.

List/Subject *x*—List active messages with *x* in their title.

LOcal—Display information of interest to local node users.

Newuser—Display information especially targeted at new users.

Quit—Disconnect from cluster.

Read—Read oldest message not read by you.

Read *n*—Read message numbered *n*.

Read/Nopage *n*—Read message numbered *n* without being prompted to display next page of message.

REPly—Reply to the last message read by you.

REPly/Delete—Reply to and delete the last message read by you.

REPly/RR—Reply to the last message read by you and send a return receipt message back to you when your reply is read.

Send—Send a message.

Send *x*—Send a message to station whose call sign is *x*.

Send/NOPrivate—Send a public message.

Send/NOPrivate *x*—Send a public message to station whose call sign is *x*.

Send/Private—Send a private message.

Send/Private *x*—Send a private message to station whose call sign is *x*.

SEt/ALias *x*—Inform the cluster that you wish to use an alias call sign *x*.

SEt/ANSi—Inform the cluster that your DTE is ANSI-compatible.

SEt/ANSi/Alt—Inform the cluster that your DTE is ANSI-compatible, but recognizes the alternate reverse video sequence <ESC> G 4.

SEt/BEep—Enable sounding the beep alert for all announcements from the cluster.

SEt/DX_announcements—Disable sending DX announcements to your station.

SEt/Filter/*m*/BAND=*b x*—Inform the cluster which DX country announcements you do not want sent to your station, where *m* is the operating mode(s) (CW, SSB or RTTY), *b* is the frequency band(s) and *x* is the country prefix(s).

SEt/NOFilter/*m*/BAND=*b x*—Inform the cluster which DX country announcements you want sent to your station, where *m* is the operating mode(s) (CW, SSB or RTTY), *b* is the frequency band(s) and *x* is the country prefix(s).

SEt/Here—Inform the cluster that you are in your radio shack.

SEt/HOMe_node *x*—Inform the cluster that *x* is call sign of your "home node," that is, the node you usually connect with and where you wish to receive mail.

SEt/LOCATion *a b c d e f*—Inform the cluster that your station's latitude is *a* degrees *b* minutes north or south (*c*) and longitude *d* degrees *e* minutes east or west (*f*), for example, SE/LOCAT 41 33 N 73 0 W.

SEt/LOGin_announcements—Enable sending log-in announcements to your station when you connect to a node.

SEt/MAIL_announcements—Enable sending "new mail" announcements to your station.

SEt/Name *x*—Inform the cluster that your name is *x*.

SEt/NEed *x*—Store in the cluster's database that you need country(s) whose prefix(s) is *x* on CW and SSB, for example, SE/NE XX9.

SEt/NEed/BAND=(*b*) *x*—Store in the cluster's database that on frequency band(s) *b*, you need country(s) whose prefix(s) is *x*, for example, SE/NE/BAND=(10) ZS9.

SEt/NEed/*m* *x*—Store in the cluster's database that in mode *m* (where *m* equals CW, SSB or RTTY), you need country(s) whose prefix(s) is *x*, for example, SE/NE/RTTY YA.

SEt/NEed/*m*/BAND=(*b*) *x*—Store in the cluster's database that in operating mode *m* (where *m* equals CW, SSB or RTTY), on frequency band(s) *b*, you need country(s) whose prefix(s) is *x*, for example, SE/NE/CW/BAND=(10) YA.

SEt/NOALias—Inform the cluster that you do not wish to use an alias call sign.

SEt/NOAnsi—Inform the cluster that your DTE is not ANSI-compatible.

SEt/NOBEep—Disable sounding the beep alert for all announcements from the cluster.

SEt/NODX_announcement—Disables sending DX announcements to your station only during your current connection to the cluster.

SEt/NOHere—Inform the cluster that you are not in your shack.

SEt/NOLOGin_announcements—Disable sending log-in announcements to your station when you connect to a node.

SEt/NOMAIL_announcements—Disable sending "new mail" announcements to your station only during your current connection to the cluster.

SEt/NOPRIVIlege—Disable SYSOP privileges.

SEt/NOTAlk—Disable sending talk messages to your station.

SEt/NOWWV—Disable sending WWV announcements to your station.

SEt/Page *n*—Inform the cluster that you want *n* lines to be sent for display as a page on your terminal.

SEt/PRIVIlege—Enable SYSOP privileges.

SEt/Qth *u*—Inform the cluster your QTH is town or city is *x*.

SEt/TAlk—Enable sending talk messages to your station.

SEt/WWV—Enable sending WWV announcements to your station.

SHow/ANNouncements—Display the previous cluster announcements.

SHow/ANNouncements *x*—Display the previous cluster announcements that included specified text (*x*).

SHow/ANNouncements/*n*—Display a specified number (*n*) of previous cluster announcements.

SHow/Archive—Display names of files in archive file area.

(Continued on next page)

SHow/BULLAddr—Display list of bulletin addresses.

SHow/Bulletins—Display names of files in bulletin file area.

SHow/CLuster—Display number of nodes in cluster, number of local users, number of total users, maximum number of connected stations and the length of time since last system reboot.

SHow/COMmands—Display available Show commands.

SHow/Configuration—Display physical configuration of cluster.

SHow/Configuration *x*—Display list of stations connected to node whose call sign is *x*.

SHow/Configuration/Nodes—Display list of locally connected nodes and list of nodes connectable via locally connected nodes.

SHow/DAte—Display date.

SHow/Distro—Display mail distribution list.

SHow/Distro *x*—Display mail distribution list named *x*.

SHow/DX— Display the last five DX announcements.

SHow/DX *b*—Display the last five DX announcements for frequency band *b*, for example, SH/DX 14.

SHow/DX *b x*—Display the last five DX announcements on frequency band *b* for country prefix *x*, for example, SH/DX 28 BV.

SHow/DX *f1-f2*—Display the last five DX announcements between operating frequency *f1* and *f2*, for example, SH/DX 14000-14075

SHow/DX/D*n*—Display the DX announcements for a specified number (*n*) of previous days.

SHow/DX/*n*—Display a specified number (*n*) of previous DX announcements, for example, SH/DX/10.

SHow/DX/*n b*—Display a specified number (*n*) of previous DX announcements for frequency band *b*, for example, SH/DX/20 21.

SHow/DX/*n b x*—Display a specified number (*n*) of previous DX announcements on frequency band *b* for country prefix *x*, for example, SH/DX/15 7 XE.

SHow/Exclude—Display list of stations excluded from receiving output from cluster node.

SHow/FILES—Display names of files in general files area.

SHow/FILTER *x*—Display list of frequency bands for which DX country announcements will not be sent to your station for country prefix(s) *x*.

SHow/FOrward—Display mail-forwarding database.

SHow/Heading *x*—Display heading and distance to country whose prefix is *x*.

SHow/Inactivity—Display status of inactivity function and, if enabled, the inactivity timer value.

SHow/LOCation *x*—Display the longitude and latitude of station whose call sign is *x*.

SHow/LOGOn-messages—Display log-in announcements that are sent to your station when you connect to a node.

SHow/Muf *x*—Display maximum usable frequency (MUF) for country whose prefix is *x*.

SHow/NEeds *x*—Display needed countries for station whose call sign is *x*.

SHow/NEeds *x*—Display stations needing country whose prefix is *x*.

SHow/NEeds/*m* *x*—Display needed countries for mode *m* (where *m* equals CW, SSB or RTTY) for station whose call sign is *x*.

SHow/NOTice—Display system notice.

SHow/Prefix *x*—Display country prefix(s) starting with letter(s) *x*.

SHow/STation *x*—Display station information for call sign *x*.

SHow/SUn—Display local sunrise and sunset times.

SHow/SUn *x*—Display sunrise and sunset times for country whose prefix is *x*.

SHow/Time—Display local time.

SHow/Time *x*—Display time for country whose prefix is *x*.

SHow/Users—Display call signs of stations connected to the cluster.

SHow/Users *x*—Display name and location of station whose call sign is *x*.

SHow/Version—Display version of the cluster software.

SHow/Wwv—Display last five WWV propagation announcements.

SHow/Wwv/*n*—Display specified number (*n*) of previous WWV propagation announcements.

SHow/WX—Display recent weather announcements.

SHow/*x*—Display names of files in file area named *x*.

SWitch—Use alias call sign.

Talk *x*—Talk to station whose call sign is *x*.

Talk *x m*—Send one-line message *m* to station whose call sign is *x*.

TYpe *x*—Display a file named *x*.

TYpe/*z*/*n* *x*—Display a specified number of lines (*n*) of file named *x* stored in file area named *z*.

TYpe/*n* *x*—Display a specified number of lines (*n*) of file named *x*.

TYpe/NOPAGE *x*—Display file named *x* without pausing at the end of each page.

TYpe/*z* *x*—Display file named *x* stored in file area named *z*.

UPDate/*x*—Update the database named *x* (by overwriting it).

UPDate/*x*/APPEND—Update the database named *x* by appending to it.

Upload/Bulletin—Upload a bulletin.

Upload/Files—Upload a file.

Upload/Usercmd—Upload a personal command procedure.

Upload/*x*—Upload a file to file area named *x*.

WWV SF=*n1*,A=*n2*,K=*n3*,*x*—Announce and log WWV propagation information where *n1* is the solar flux, *n2* is the A-index, *n3* is the K-index and *x* is the forecast.

WX *x*—Announce weather information *x*.

11

Gateways

It all started because the computer that Hank Oredson, WØRLI, used to build his PBBS had two serial ports. Hank only needed one port for his VHF radio equipment and TNC. But, waste not, want not, so Hank put the second port to work, too, and designed his PBBS to allow the first port to gateway to the second port.

By invoking the gateway command, a user who was connected to the PBBS's first port could communicate via whatever communication equipment was connected to the second port, for example, a TNC and another VHF radio, a UHF radio, a HF radio or, instead of a TNC, a telephone line modem connected to telephone line network! If the TNC on the first port was connected to a 2-meter transceiver and the TNC on the second port was connected to an HF transceiver, a PBBS user on 2 meters could use the gateway to make packet radio connections on HF. Fig 9-2 in the Bulletin Board chapter illustrates the gateway function.

The gateway function became an integral part of most of the PBBS designs that followed WØRLI's system. It also became an integral part of various packet radio networking schemes that followed. For example, you can connect to a NET/ROM node on 2 meters and command that node to connect you to another node on a different 2-meter channel or a different band be it VHF, UHF or HF.

WORMHOLES

A wormhole is a communication link that utilizes a non-Amateur Radio medium. For example, commercial satellites are occasionally used for wormholes. In 1987, an

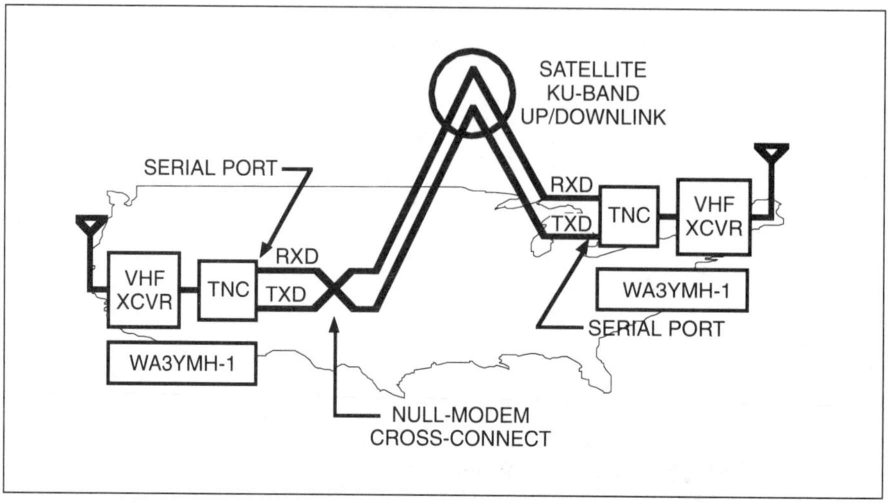

Figure 11-1— The old WA3YMH-1 wormhole acted as a digipeater with a coverage area that encompassed parts of the East and West Coasts of the United States.

experimental satellite link between packet radio network nodes located in California and Maryland provided a temporary one-hop connection between packet radio stations on the United States East and West Coasts. Mike Bach, WB6FFC, was co-founder of the Vitalink Communications Corporation, and it was Vitalink's commercial geosynchronous satellite that provided the transcontinental wormhole. The satellite provided the interconnection between the serial ports of the TNCs on each coast. The call sign of the operation was WA3YMH-1. It is no longer in operation, but new satellite wormholes have been activated since its demise. Fig 11-1 illustrates how wormholes work.

GATEWAY OPERATING TECHNIQUES

Using a gateway, whether it has a wormhole or not, is simple. Connect to your local PBBS and use its Help function to find the gateway command(s). If your local PBBS is a WØRLI (or compatible) PBBS, there are two gateway commands that will be useful.

To find out what is going on at the other end of the gateway, invoke the Monitor Gateway command:

Monitor *portn* <CR>

where *portn* is the number of the PBBS's port for the gateway. The Monitor Gateway command will allow you to find out what stations are active at the remote end of the gateway. If you hear a station you wish to contact, invoke the Connect via Gateway command:

Connect *portn W1AW* <CR>

where *portn* is the number of the PBBS's port for the gateway and *W1AW* is the call sign of the station you wish to contact. Once the connection across the gateway is completed, you can communicate across the gateway in the same manner you would communicate with any other connected packet station. When you are through, use the Disconnect command to break the connection.

Gatewaying via network nodes is a little trickier. You first connect to your local node, then enter the Nodes command:

Nodes <CR>

The Nodes command will cause your local node to send you a list of nodes that are connectable from that local node. Now, here is the tricky part: trying to pick out a gateway from that list.

There are no rules for naming nodes and, similarly there are no rules for naming node gateways. Picking a node is like buying a pig in a poke, but I will try and give you some guidance. If the nodes list contains node names that are similar to the name of the node you are using, it is likely to be a gateway for that node. For example, if you are connected to a local node named KONG3 and the nodes list for KONG3 contains nodes named KONG1, KONG2 and KONG4, it is likely that they are gateways. Problem is that you have no idea where you will end up if you use gateways with nondescript names. The node, itself, may be able to offer some assistance by means of its Info and Routes command (if the node supports those commands).

Once you have determined which node gateway you wish to use, enter the Connect command as follows:

Connect *NODEGW* <CR>

where *NODEGW* is the call sign or mnemonic identifier of the node gateway.

After completing the gateway connection with the distant node, you can monitor the gateway to find stations you wish to contact and connect and communicate with those stations across the gateway. Use the Disconnect command to break the connection when you are done.

GATEWAYS TO THE INTERNET

The Internet is a agglomeration of TCP/IP networks that connects universities, research institutions, high-technology companies, and so on, throughout the world. Today, there are a number of gateways between the Internet and the amateur packet radio TCP/IP network, the AMPRNet. Like the WØRLI PBBS gateways, the Internet-to-packet radio gateways are actually computers in nearly a dozen countries that are connected to both the AMPRNet and the Internet.

These gateways use the Internet as a high-speed conduit to carry packets between geographically dispersed segments of the AMPRNet. The packets may be native AMPRNet (TCP/IP) packets or they may be plain vanilla AX.25 and NET/ROM packets.

It is possible to set up a computer to be active on both networks because the TCP/IP protocols implemented for Amateur Radio by Phil Karn, KA9Q, are basically the same as those used on the Internet. Phil did add a feature to his TCP/IP software (*NOS*), which allows an AX.25, NET/ROM or another TCP/IP packet to be encapsulated in a packet carried over the Internet.

In the Beginning, Internet Begot AMPRNet

The AMPRNet is actually part of the Internet. Thanks to the efforts of Hank Magnuski, KA6M, in the early 1980s, Amateur Radio operators were assigned their own Internet *domain*, that is, a subsection of the Internet called *ampr.org* with a large block of node (IP) addresses (Internet node addresses beginning with 44 are Amateur Radio stations).

Although the AMPRNet is a legitimate part of the Internet, technical and legal issues have given it a special status. Unlike other networks that are part of the Internet, the AMPRNet is divided into regional subnetworks that were not connected to each other until gateways came into existence. Amateur Radio regulations that bar the introduction of non-amateur traffic onto Amateur Radio channels make it impossible to indiscriminately link AMPRNet with the rest of the Internet [which is the usual approach of unifying other regional (non-Amateur Radio) subnetworks]. However, there is no legal problem using the Internet as a speedy connection between two Amateur Radio stations when a ham on one end or the other is initiating all the packets. And that is exactly how gateways bring the AMPRNet subnetworks around the world together.

Besides surmounting the legal and technical issues, gateways would not exist were it not for the gracious sponsorship of universities and companies that allow their ham students and employees to use their Internet connections and facilities. With such support, these organizations are enhancing the capabilities of Amateur Radio for research, education, emergency traffic handling and other important functions.

Services up Front

First and foremost, the gateways link AMPRNet subnetworks that are scattered all over the world. Thanks to my local gateway, I can now establish SMTP (mail), Telnet (remote terminal), FTP (file transfer) and finger (user information) connections directly with other amateur TCP/IP stations in different parts of the U.S. and other countries.

In many cases, TCP/IP users can also connect directly to the gateways (or to neighboring machines set up specifically to provide end-user services) to access weather data, call sign information, chat servers, etc. Most of the gateways also offer these services to AX.25 users and sometimes to NET/ROM users as well.

Services in the Background

The gateways also enhance AX.25 and NET/ROM users' enjoyment of packet radio without those users having to connect to a gateway or even being aware that a gateway exists. For example, some regional PacketCluster networks are using gateways to connect to each other, like the Northern California DX Packet Spotting Network. At times, this network is linked to similar networks in Texas, the Pacific Northwest and Europe via a nearby AMPRNet/Internet gateway.

Other common "hidden" uses of the gateways are carrying PBBS mail and connecting geographically dispersed NET/ROM nodes. A gateway in Hawaii and an accompanying satellite gateway have nearly supplanted HF packet channels for moving PBBS bulletins in and out of the Aloha State. NET/ROM users who see dozens of nodes from all over the world are often seeing an AMPRNet/Internet gateway in action.

How to Use the Internet-to-Packet Radio Gateways

Because the list of gateways changes frequently (new ones come on line and others disappear as hams who run them graduate or change jobs), the best way to find out if there is one in your area is to ask around your local packet radio community, especially the TCP/IP users. If there is a gateway near you, check with its SYSOP to find out the exact policies and technical requirements for using it. Maybe one day soon, you will find yourself FTP'ing a file from a packet station in Sweden or exchanging mail with a ham in Australia.

There is misinformation and misconceptions floating around packet radio about how to use the Internet-to-packet radio gateways because no two gateways are exactly alike. As a result, it is not possible to provide specific instructions that explain how to use them all. On the other hand, instructions that are too general will be so lacking in information that you will get little or nothing out of them.

The third alternative (the one I've chosen to use here) is to provide specific instructions on how to use a particular Internet-to-packet radio gateway. After reading them, you should understand how to use one gateway and be able to apply that knowledge to other gateways you may want to use. Although other gateways you encounter may not work exactly the same as the one described here, they'll be similar enough so that you won't have to be completely reeducated when you use a different gateway.

Jim Durham, W2XO, Gibsonia, Pennsylvania, runs a popular packet-to-Internet gateway and has generously agreed to allow me to use his gateway as the example for properly using packet-to-Internet gateways.

The gateway is configured to make mailing from the ham packet radio network to and from the Internet as straightforward as possible and in accordance with standard mail gatewaying practices. You use the subject lines and message text as usual (you don't need any special lines in the text or subject of the message). However, Internet users have to register with W2XO so that he can assign an alias to you, as explained below.

Mailing from the Internet to Packet Radio

To send a message to a packet radio station from the Internet, you have to replace the ham packet radio address' at-symbol with a percentage sign, follow that with an at-symbol and then the gateway's Internet address (in this case, w2xo.pgh.pa.us). For example, to mail a message from the Internet to packet radio address WA1LOU@ W1EDH.CT.USA.NOAM, you modify the address as follows:

original packet radio address: WA1LOU@W1EDH.CT.USA.NOAM
replace @ with %: WA1LOU%W1EDH.CT.USA.NOAM
follow result with @: WA1LOU%W1EDH.CT.USA.NOAM@
add gateway's Internet address: WA1LOU%W1EDH.CT.USA.NOAM@ w2xo.pgh.pa.us

You use this modified address to originate mail from the Internet for delivery to an amateur packet radio station via an Internet-to-packet radio gateway.

Mailing from Packet Radio to the Internet

The amateur packet radio message format permits a maximum of six characters in the recipient's address. W2XO uses an alias to get around this limitation, which would prevent you from using an Internet address like f.williamson@foobley.com to originate a message from packet radio. If the Internet recipient is a ham, W2XO uses the recipient's call sign as the alias. If the recipient isn't a ham, he creates a six-character alias in the form 3PTYXX (third-party xx).

To send a message to an Internet recipient from the amateur packet radio network via an Internet-to-packet radio gateway, you address the message to the recipient's call sign or alias followed by @W2XO.#SWPA.PA.USA.NOAM. When the message arrives at the W2XO gateway, the gateway looks up the call sign or alias to find the corresponding Internet address for relaying the message via the Internet.

For example, to send a message from amateur packet radio to horzepa@gdc.com on the Internet, you use Horzepa's call sign (if he has one) followed by the at-sign and the gateway's packet radio address. In this case, the resulting address would be WA1LOU@W2XO.#SWPA.PA.USA.NOAM. If horzepa@gdc.com does not have a call sign, W2XO assigns Horzepa an alias like 3PTY73 and you send your message to horzepa@gdc.com using the alias followed by the gateway's packet radio address. In this case, the resulting address would be 3PTY73@W2XO.#SWPA.PA.USA.NOAM. In either case, when your message arrives at the W2XO gateway, the gateway looks up WA1LOU or 3PTY73, finds the corresponding Internet address (horzepa@gdc.com) and sends it on its Internet way.

CONCLUSION

Gateways provide the tools that allow packet radio operators to expand their horizons beyond basic VHF packet operation and literally work the world.

12

APRS

Like the *WØRLI Mailbox*, NET/ROM, *NOS* and the DX *PacketCluster*, before it, *APRS* (Automatic Packet Reporting System) is the latest application to take packet radio by storm. The purpose of APRS is to apply packet radio to real-time events where information must be relayed quickly. Not only does APRS accomplish this purpose, but it does it graphically by displaying the information on maps displayed on the user's computer screen.

APRS sends and receives station location information or *positions* from different types of stations: homes, portables, mobiles, digipeaters, nodes, DX clusters, mailboxes, etc. The station positions contain, at a minimum, the following information: latitude, longitude and the *station type*. These packets are sent as unconnected packets (unnumbered information or Ul Frames—see Appendix A). APRS receives these packets, processes the information contained therein and displays an appropriate symbol on a map showing the location of the station.

Besides being able to transmit station positions, users can also send information about an *object*, that is, something that is not an amateur packet radio station. For example, you can transmit the position of a thunderstorm passing through your area (before you pull the big switch) by giving its latitude, longitude and station type, which in this case would be a thunderstorm. The position of the thunderstorm will appear on the map of everyone using APRS on that channel. By the way, 145.79, 445.925, and a center frequency of 10.1483 MHz are the national APRS operating frequencies. FM serves as the operating mode on VHF and UHF, while LSB does the honors on HF.

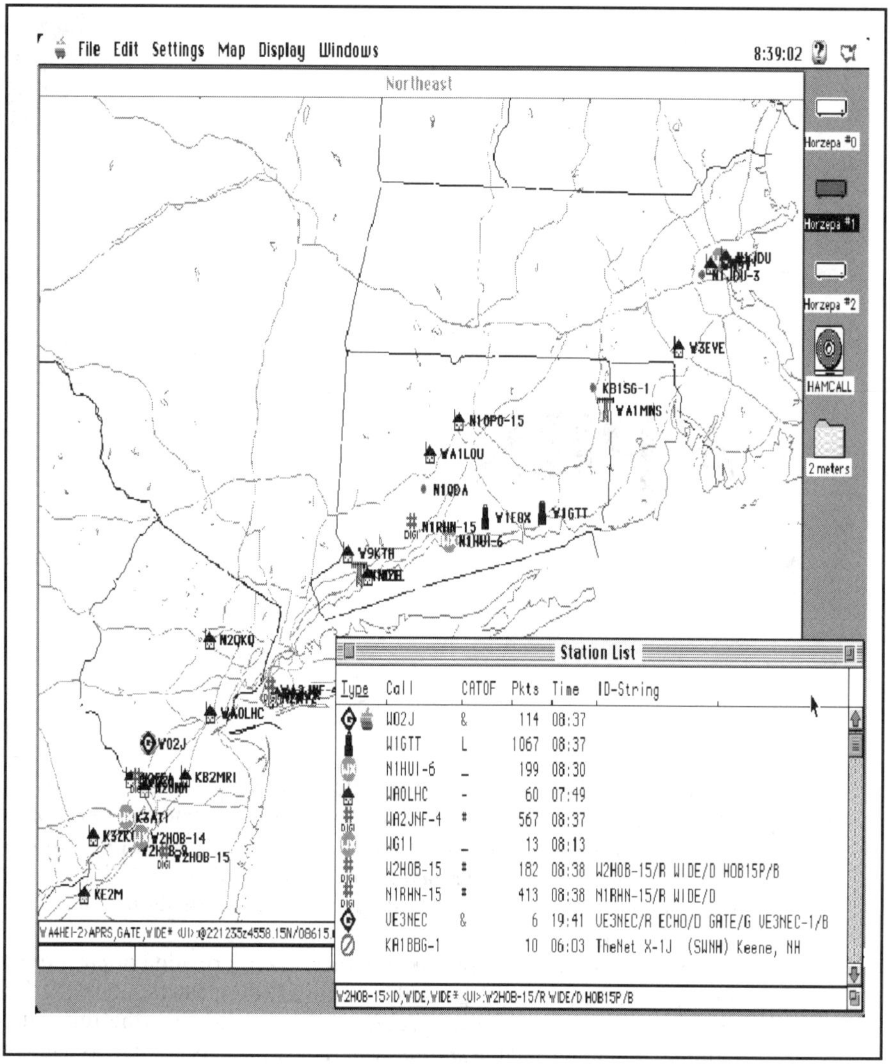

Fig 12-1—*MacAPRS* running at the WA1LOU lab in downtown Wolcott, Connecticut.

Long-time packet radio guru, Bob Bruninga, WB4APR, developed APRS and released it to the world as an IBM-PC/MS-DOS computer program in 1992. In 1994, the Macs brothers, Keith and Mark Sproul, WU2Z and KB2ICI, released *MacAPRS*, the Macintosh implementation of APRS. Bob, Keith and Mark agreed to work together in order to keep APRS and MacAPRS in sync, that is, completely compatible.

WHY APRS?

APRS is the result of WB4APR's long experience trying to use packet radio for real-time communications and public service events. Bob felt that packet radio had great potential, but, before APRS, it had been used mostly for passing large volumes of message traffic from point-to-point or into the national traffic distribution system. It had been difficult to apply packet to real-time events where information has a very short life span because, typically, several steps are involved in preparing and passing messages including decisions about routing and connectivity.

WB4APR designed APRS based on his observation that most events, emergencies, exercises, weather nets and general communications spend more time concerned with where things are and where they are going than any other single identifiable category. APRS begins to suggest the potential for tactical communications using amateur packet radio. Furthermore, it attempts to define a standard format using *UI* frames for object positioning and reporting that could be universally applicable in Amateur Radio.

HOW DOES APRS WORK?

APRS avoids the complexity and limitations of trying to maintain a connected network. It permits any number of stations to participate and exchanges data just like voice users would on a single voice net. Any station that has information to contribute simply transmits it and all the stations receive it and log it.

Although APRS mapping capability was developed to display the movement of *Global Positioning System* (GPS) devices interfaced to packet radio, most of the features evolved from earlier efforts to support real-time packet radio communications at special events. Any person in the network, upon learning where an object or asset is located, can move his cursor and place the object on his screen. This action is then transmitted to all screens in the network so everyone gains, in a glance, the combined knowledge of all network participants. Furthermore, the map screen retains all the information for future reference. Moving objects can be dead-reckoned to their current locations with one key stroke and all this can be accomplished without using a single GPS device.

The availability of GPS cards for under $300 today is icing on the cake. With a GPS card, TNC and hand-held transceiver all stuffed in a box, almost any object can be tracked. For example, this technology has been installed in a football helmet for the Army-Navy football game run, on bicycles for a marathon event, and, of course, in motor vehicles—and onboard a cow!

APRS APPLICATIONS

APRS is an excellent tool for triangulating the location of a hidden transmitter. To use APRS in this manner, each station having a bearing or signal strength on a target, enters that bearing by means of the OPS-DF command. His station then reports its location and its line of bearing or a signal strength contour for the target. All stations running APRS will see any reported direction-finding bearing lines on their maps. Furthermore, if a direction-finding vehicle has a GPS or LORAN device onboard, it can be tracked and directed right to the location of the target.

APRS may also be a solution to the effective use of orbiting packet radio digipeaters such as on the American shuttles and the Russian space station *Mir*. The problem with space digipeaters is saturation on the uplink channel, which makes the use of a normal connected protocol impractical. For a connected contact, a total of five successive and successful packet transmissions are required. Not only does APRS reduce this to one packet, but it also capitalizes on the most fascinating aspect of the Amateur Radio hobby, that is, the display on a map of the location of those stations. If all stations simply inserted their latitude and longitude as the first 19 characters of their beacon text, everyone within the satellite footprint would see the location of every successful uplink. Since the shuttle is a rapidly moving object, the locations of successful uplink stations will move progressively along the ground track. No changes onboard the shuttle or *Mir* would be required to accomplish this.

APRS position reports can also contain weather information. The ULTIMETER-II home weather stations can be interfaced to APRS to automatically provide the weather information for transmission in APRS unconnected packets. APRS users can also set weather alarms to be alerted when severe weather conditions occur.

APRS is also an ideal tool for DX cluster users. Not only do all DX spots appear on an APRS map, but by operating in the monitor mode, the APRS user reduces the overall packet load on the DX cluster channel. Also the APRS monitoring station sees a DX spot as soon as it is sent to the first station, rather than later on in the queue.

APRS FUNDAMENTALS

APRS and *Mac*APRS are very easy to use. Beforehand, the only thing you need is latitude and longitude of your station. If possible, find out your coordinates in degrees, minutes and seconds because the more accurate your coordinates are, the more accurate will be your position on the APRS maps. The coordinates of your station may be obtained from a number of sources; U.S. Geological Survey topographical maps are the best.

Start the software and enter the coordinates of your station into the station settings of the program. Also, enter your station call sign and alias. The alias depends on the kind of station you are operating. If your station is going to act as a digipeater or if it has a gateway to another APRS operating frequency all affect what the alias will be. The typical non-digipeater home station with a single port TNC will have an alias of "wide." The Unproto parameter of your TNC will have to be similarly set. Also, depending on the brand and model of your TNC, other TNC parameters will have to be set (refer to the software documentation for specifics). In general, CONStamp, HEaderln, MCOM and MStamp must be off and Monitor must be on.

Once all these parameters are set and your radio is tuned to an APRS operating frequency, select a map, sit back and watch what happens!

APRS RESOURCES

AEA's PK-12 TNC and all current PacComm TNCs have firmware that is compatible with GPS equipment. PacComm even has a TNC (the TINY-2 MK-2/GPS) that has a built-in GPS receiver. AEA also has an adapter cable that allows the user to connect a TNC and a GPS receiver to the same COM port of a DOS-class computer.

The best source for the most current APRS software, both the DOS and Macintosh versions, is the TAPR Internet site. As soon as a new version of software is released, it is available for ftp'ing from ftp.tapr.org and www.tapr.org. Go to directory tapr/SIG/aprssig/files, then go to /dosstuff/APRSdos, /macstuff/MacAPRS or /winstuff/ WinAPRS for the DOS, Macintosh and Windows versions of APRS, respectively. The software is also available from the usual gang of sources: other Internet sites, BBSs and computer on-line services.

WB4APR's creation is a powerful tool that can be used to perform a variety of tasks, yet is very simple to use. As a result, it has the potential to become a very important application in amateur packet radio.

13

Outer Space

Packet radio in outer space is not science fiction. It is a real mode of packet radio communications...as real as your local packet BBS or DX packet cluster. And it is being used by hams all over the world to push out the envelope of the state of the art.

Outer space packet radio comes in two varieties: the ham-made modes and the natural modes. First, I will describe what hams have wrought to transfer packets via outer space, then I will describe outer space packet radio by means that nature has provided.

TNCS IN SPACE

For over a decade, hams have sent TNCs into outer space aboard manned and unmanned spacecraft. Various American shuttle missions and the Russian space station *Mir* represent the manned spacecraft that have had TNCs onboard, while a variety of Amateur Radio satellites (the OSCARs and their descendants) have provided unmanned platforms for TNCs in orbit.

Amateur Radio entered the space age when Orbiting Satellite Carrying Amateur Radio Number 1, better known as OSCAR I, was launched on December 12, 1961. The development of the technology that put man (and OSCAR) in space required advances in electronics that resulted in today's computer technology. Since the computer age is a result of the space program, and packet radio is a child of the computer age, it is only fitting that the circle be completed as packet radio enters space onboard manned spacecraft and Amateur Radio satellites.

The Early Right Stuff

The plans for future packet radio networks place heavy emphasis on orbiting packet radio transponders. Before these plans were implemented, experiments were conducted to determine if they were practical.

The practicality of packet radio space communications was tested and proven on March 11, 1984, when OSCAR 10 was successfully used as a repeater to connect packet radio stations on the East and West Coasts of the United States. Later that year (on October 28), packet radio stations in various parts of North America used OSCAR 10 to access a PBBS located in Maryland. During a 60-minute period of this experiment, one station successfully downloaded 50 Kbytes of data from the PBBS via the satellite!

Another step towards a space-based packet radio network was completed on January 16, 1985, when the Digital Communications Experiment (DCE) aboard UoSat-OSCAR 11 was first used. The DCE was built to show that low orbiting satellites could be used to store and forward packet radio messages. In January 1985, messages were sent and received by stations in Hawaii, California and England using OSCAR 11. These experiments led to packet radio satellite operations that are currently on the air or in the works.

Table 13-1
Digital Transponder Frequencies and Modes

Satellite	***Uplink(s) (MHz)***	***Downlink(s) (MHz)***	***Data Format***
AMSAT-OSCAR-16	145.90 FM 145.92 FM 145.94 FM 145.96 FM	437.025 SSB 2401.10 SSB	1200 bit/s PSK AX.25
DOVE-OSCAR-17	None	145.825 FM 2401.22	Digitized voice with 1200 bit/s AFSK AX.25 telemetry
WEBERSAT-OSCAR-18	None	437.075 SSB 437.10 SSB	1200 bit/s PSK AX.25
LUSAT-OSCAR-19	145.84 FM 145.86 FM 145.88 FM 145.90 FM	437.125 SSB 437.15 SSB	1200 bit/s PSK AX.25
UoSAT-OSCAR 22	145.90 FM 145.975 FM	435.120 FM	9600 bit/s FSK AX.25
KITSAT-OSCAR 23	145.85 FM 145.90 FM	435.175 FM	9600 bit/s FSK AX.25
KITSAT-OSCAR 25	145.87 FM 145.98 FM	436.50 FM	9600 bit/s FSK AX.25
ITAMSAT-OSCAR 26	145.875 FM 145.900 FM 145.925 FM 145.950 FM	435.870 SSB	1200 bit/s PSK AX.25

Source: *The ARRL Operating Manual* (Newington, CT: ARRL 1995)

Real-Time vs. Store-and-Forward Communications

Packet radio communications via satellite fall into two broad categories: real-time communications and store-and-forward communications. In real-time satellite communications, a satellite relays packets immediately from one station to another, acting like a digipeater on a very, very high hill. In store-and-forward communications, the satellite acts like an orbiting PBBS, storing messages as it passes over one station and relaying them later as it passes over another part of the Earth.

During real-time communications, all stations that want to exchange packets must be able to "see" the satellite at once, so satellites in high orbits are used. For store-and-forward communications, the satellite can be in a low Earth orbit, and the Earth's rotation will take the on-board PBBS within range of everywhere on the Earth at least once a day. Both kinds of satellite packet radio communications have been tested in the Amateur Satellite Service, and each type will play a role in future packet radio networks.

During the past decade, the trend in packet radio satellite operations is toward more store-and-forward operations and less real-time communications. As a result, most packet radio satellite operations today are of the store-and-forward variety. A short description of each active packet radio satellite follows. (Table 13-1 lists the Amateur Radio satellites that are packet radio active at the time of writing this chapter.)

AMSAT-OSCAR-16 (AO-16) was sponsored by AMSAT-NA (North America), AO-16 was known as a *MicroSat*, one of the four diminutive (9-inch cube) satellites launched on January 22, 1990. It carries a 2-meter-to-70-cm store-and-forward packet radio transponder.

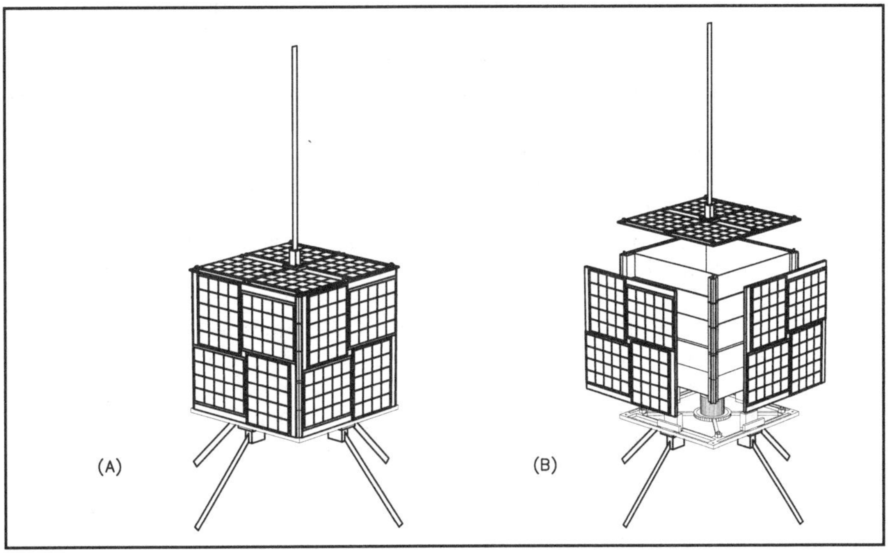

Fig 13-1—Two views of a MicroSat. Drawing A shows the satellite with its covers on; Drawing B is an exploded view revealing the exterior solar panels and the five "trays" or internal modules that contain the satellite's circuitry and make it structurally sound. *(Drawings courtesy of Dick Jansson, WD4FAB)*

DOVE-OSCAR-17 (DO-17) was another MicroSat, this one sponsored by AMSAT-Brazil, transmits packet and digitized voice messages on 2 meters.

WEBERSAT-OSCAR-18 (WO-18) was sponsored by Weber State University. This MicroSat carries a 2-meter-to-70-cm store-and-forward packet radio transponder and a small television camera that provides Earth imaging that is relayed to Earth via packet radio.

LUSAT-OSCAR-19 (LO-19) was Argentina's MicroSat carrying a 2-meter-to-70-cm store-and-forward packet radio transponder.

UoSAT-OSCAR 22 (UO-22) was designed by The University of Surrey in the United Kingdom with 9600 bit/s store-and-forward capabilities.

KITSAT-OSCAR 23 (KO-23) Korea's first Amateur Radio satellite. It was launched in 1992 with 9600 bit/s capability.

KITSAT-OSCAR 25 (KO-25) was another Korean bird with 9600 bit/s capability, launched in September 1993.

ITAMSAT-OSCAR 26 (IO-26) was Italy's entry in the Amateur Radio satellite field. It was launched in September 1993 with KO-25, and offers 1200 bit/s store-and-forward operations.

Packet Satellite Requirements

I do not intend to provide a primer on Amateur Radio satellite communications in this section (there are whole books devoted to the subject, for example, *The Satellite Experimenter's Handbook* by Martin R. Davidoff, K2UBC, published by the ARRL). Instead, this section will provide you with the specific requirements, in addition to an Amateur Radio satellite station, that you need to use the packet radio satellites.

You need a TNC, of course. However, an off-the-shelf TNC will not always do the trick. The modems built into most TNCs provide audio frequency shift keying (AFSK) modulation, whereas, most of the packet radio satellites use frequency shift keying (FSK) or phase shift keying (PSK) modulation techniques. Therefore, you will need an external modem for satellite operation, not to mention a TNC that will accept an external modem.

For AO-16, WO-18, LO-19 and IO-26A, you will need a 1200 bit/s PSK modem transmitting FM on 2 meters and receiving SSB on 70 cm, and for UO-22, KO-23 and KO-25, you will need a 9600 bit/s FSK modem transmitting FM on 2 meters and receiving FM on 70 cm (the current design of the 9600 bit/s modem is known as the *G3RUH modem)*. The primary sources for satellite modems are Tucson Amateur Packet Radio (TAPR), Advanced Electronic Applications (AEA), MFJ and PacComm.

Note that besides providing the proper modulation scheme, most modems compensate for *Doppler shift* by controlling the receiver's operating frequency (via the UP/DOWN microphone connector pins). [Doppler shift is the change or "shift" in frequency that occurs as a transmitter (in a satellite) moves in relationship to a stationary receiver (in your station).]

Radios that are 9600 bit/s ready are few and far between (Alinco and MFJ provide offerings). Therefore, in order to use your 9600 bit/s modem on the air, you will have to modify your radio for direct FSK modulation, a discriminator output, fast T/R switching and an IF of sufficient bandwidth and phase characteristics. Some radios can be modified to achieve these requirements, some cannot. Your mileage may vary.

In addition to special hardware, you also need special software in order to access the store-and-forward satellites. This ground station software allows you to receive broadcasts from the satellites, transfer files to and from the satellite, and process files for transfer to and from the satellite. Currently, the software comes in three flavors: an IBM DOS-based computer version (*PB*, *PHS*, *PFHADD* and *PG*), a Microsoft Windows version (*WISP*) and an Apple Macintosh version (*Broadcast*). All versions are available from AMSAT and the usual gang of sources.

Once you have the hardware and software up and running, you will be well on your way to exchanging data with the satellite of choice. Follow the recommendations in the satellite literature on how best to track satellites and receive their signals. Then, follow the steps outlined in the ground station software to interact with the satellite (the steps differ between different software packages). Working the satellites can be a little daunting at first, so practice awhile and get used to the satellite communication techniques before you upload your first file.

Hams in Space: *SAREX* and *Mir*

Packet radio *Shuttle Amateur Radio Experiments* (*SAREX*) have been conducted by various astronauts holding Amateur Radio licenses on a number of American space shuttle missions. Typical shuttle operations feature unique robot software that allow the maximum number of stations to contact the shuttle. This software recognizes a terrestrial connect request, sends a sequential contact number to the station, summarily disconnects the station and logs the contact. Beacons listing successful connections are transmitted intermittently.

Meanwhile, a variety of cosmonauts holding Amateur Radio licenses have made numerous packet radio contacts using the packet station onboard the Russian space station *Mir*. Occasionally, a cosmonaut will conduct live operator-to-operator packet radio contacts. Most packet contacts are between Earth stations and the packet mailbox system built into the *Mir*'s TNC, however.

No special packet radio equipment is required to contact either the American shuttle or *Mir* packet radio stations, as both use standard TNCs operating at 1200-bit/s. Shuttle operations usually occur on split transmit and receive frequencies on 2 meters, while *Mir* operations usually occur on simplex at 145.55 MHz. A simple connect command with the appropriate call sign is all that is needed to initiate a

Fig 13-2—Your author, WA1LOU, exchanges QSL cards with cosmonaut Musa Manarov, UV3AM, the SYSOP of U2MIR, after exchanging packets with Musa's mailbox system aboard the Russian space station *Mir*.

Working *Mir*

With hundreds of miles of snow-covered roads in this town, why do they always plow my road at 5 AM? Three inches of snow fell overnight and, like clockwork, the town plow passes by my home at 5 in the morning. If you live in a snowless clime, you cannot appreciate the noise a dump truck scraping a 36-inch-high blade across uneven asphalt can make when you are sound asleep. It makes 40 meters during a thunderstorm sound good!

The noise disturbed my sleep. As I squinted at my clock radio, I remembered that the Russian space station, *Mir*, was going to make a nearby pass in a few minutes.

A few weeks earlier, Musa Manarov, a cosmonaut aboard *Mir*, received a packet radio station. He had the station on the air a few days later using call sign U2MIR for live keyboard-to-keyboard sessions when time permitted and U2MIR-1 for a mini-PBBS operation the rest of the time. I had not yet worked U2MIR, so I thanked Mr. Plowman for waking me and bumped my way through the dark to my shack.

I powered up my station and ran the satellite tracking computer program in the real-time mode to display the current position of the spacecraft on a world map. During this orbit, *Mir* would come up from the Gulf of Mexico, cut across the Florida Panhandle and the heart of the Southeast, then follow the Eastern Seaboard up over Cape Cod, then out to sea.

I tuned my 2-meter transceiver to 145.55 MHz, switched it to the log periodic beam and aimed the antenna down the East Coast. Next, I turned on my TNC and loaded my packet radio terminal program in my computer. I also tuned my VHF-UHF scanning receiver to 145.55 MHz. It is connected to a discone antenna and a second TNC.

My computer, a Macintosh, can run multiple applications simultaneously. This permits me to use one packet radio terminal program to connect to U2MIR, while a second terminal program monitors the channel simultaneously via the second TNC. All the while, the satellite tracking program updates the position of *Mir* every minute.

There are three reasons why I use a second TNC. First, when the no-gain discone antenna starts receiving U2MIR's signals, I know that *Mir* is close and that it is time to switch my transceiver to the higher-gain vertical antenna at the top of my tower. (Lacking the ability to control the elevation of the log periodic beam, the vertical is the better antenna when the spacecraft is overhead.) Second, during a connection, my primary terminal program only displays the text of packets sent to me. The second TNC allows me to monitor supervisory packets exchanged between U2MIR and my station during a connection. Third, the equipment is available, so I might as well put it to good use.

Hears Musa

Mir came over the horizon right on schedule. U2MIR-1 was trying to make a connection with a 5-land station, while fending off other comers with "busy" disconnected mode (DM) frames/packets. The DM frames did not do much good because some stations did not get the message (that U2MIR was busy). They continued to send connect requests after receiving DM frames, which caused U2MIR to send more DM frames to the same stations.

This went on for two or three minutes and, by then, *Mir* was virtually overhead. U2MIR's signal was pounding in and I switched my transceiver to the vertical antenna. Then, U2MIR-1 sent a CQ beacon packet. I already had typed "C U2MIR-1" into my computer, so when I saw the beacon, I pounced on the Enter key to send a connect request and, BANG!—just like that, I was connected to U2MIR-1 and received its log-on message:

Logged on to U2MIR's Personal Message System

CMD(B/H/J/K/KM/L/M/R/S/SR/V/?)>

I already had created a message for Musa, so I only had to enter three keys to send the message into space. When I received a Subject prompt, I thought that success was within my grasp. The second TNC showed U2MIR-1 sending DM frames to a few other stations in the Northeast. (The advantage of living in the upper right hand corner of the U.S. is that the number of stations I have to contend with dwindles as *Mir* whizzes past me toward the open sea (in comparison to when *Mir* is heading inland). Besides some Beantowners and a VE1, I did not have much competition, but it did prevent me from ending my message to Musa.

Near the end of the pass, it was just U2MIR and I exchanging packets as the other stations seemed to have evaporated. I was sure that I could end my message to Musa, but I never did get another PBBS CMD prompt to affirm the successful reception of my message. After *Mir* disappeared over the horizon, I started worrying that I had sent the wrong end-of-message routine. I figured <CTRL-Z> was the universal way of ending a message to a PBBS. Was my assumption in error? Did I really blow it this time?

Later, I looked it up and <CTRL-Z> should have done the trick. I guess U2MIR just never heard it.

Merely Another Connection

It is not too difficult to work *Mir*'s packet station. You don't need any exotic equipment to do it. Off-the-shelf TNCs and radio equipment are all you need. My second TNC setup is a luxury. It is useful, but you can communicate without it. An elevation rotator would do wonders for my antenna system, but lacking that I still managed to connect with the orbiting packet radio station. If you thought about equipping your station for the MicroSats, UoSats and the other packet radio satellites, *Mir* provides an opportunity to try outer space packet radio without getting new equipment.

Here are some operating tips to make it easier for everyone.

- Don't transmit until you hear *Mir*. Sometimes the cosmonauts operate voice, so sending packets then will prove fruitless and be a nuisance.
- Turn on TNC parameters MON, MCOM and MALL so you can get a feel for what is transpiring between *Mir* and the ground stations. Monitoring supervisory packets should prevent you from unintentionally transmitting while *Mir* is connecting with or connected to another station.
- If you should receive a busy DM frame, sit back and wait until you see *Mir*'s CQ beacon before transmitting another connect request.
- If you do connect with the Mir packet mailbox system, make sure you log-out one or two minutes before the space station gets below 10 degrees above your horizon.
- Have fun!

connection with either manned space vehicle. The accompanying sidebar titled "Working *Mir*," describes how this author successfully worked *Mir* using his "average" amateur packet radio station. It was a "piece of cake."

NATURAL SPACE COMMUNICATIONS

In addition to the packet radio satellite and manned spacecraft operations, amateur packet radio operators have conducted experiments using natural space objects for packet radio communication. Amateurs have bounced packets off the ionized trails of meteors entering the Earth's atmosphere and have bounced packets off our natural satellite, the moon.

Meteor Scatter

As space debris (meteors) enters the Earth's atmosphere, friction between the debris and the atmosphere causes the debris to burn up, leaving a very temporary ionized trail in their wake. This temporary ionized trail can reflect VHF and UHF signals back to Earth, extending the normal propagation limits of these signals.

Before packet radio, CW and voice modes were used for meteor-scatter communications. The ionized trails are short lived, however, and very little data can be transferred using the relatively slow CW and voice modes. Several meteor trails must be used to pass enough data for a complete contact.

The solution to this problem is to use a communications mode that transfers more data in a short time. Packet radio seems perfect for this application and, on August 5, 1984, Ralph Wallio, WØRPK, in Iowa and Bob Carpenter, W3OTC, in Maryland used 6 meters to complete the first amateur packet radio meteor-scatter contact (four nights earlier, Bob received 2 percent of Ralph's meteor-scattered packets). After that first contact, the two stations continued to make 50-MHz meteor scatter contacts on a routine basis. WØRPK used 250 watts into a five-element beam antenna and W3OTC used 150 watts into a six-element beam antenna.

Fig 13-3—EME (moonbounce) work requires very high-gain antennas, like these at K1FO.

Packet lengths were limited to 30 or 40 characters and were transmitted at 1200 bit/s using AFSK FM. Later, in August 1984, an organized effort was conducted using 1200 bit/s AFSK FM transmissions on 2 meters during the Perseids meteor shower. During this effort, several stations throughout the United States, including this author's station, successfully copied beacons and connect requests via meteor scatter. On August 12, during the peak of the shower, Rich Zwirko, K1HTV, in Maryland and WØRPK completed the first 2-meter packet radio meteor-scatter contact.

Meteors are constantly entering the Earth's atmosphere. As more packet radio stations take advantage of this form of propagation, and as higher packet radio data rates are achieved, meteor-scatter packet radio can become a widely used mode of communications.

Moonbounce (EME)

Earth-to-moon-to-Earth (*EME*) or *moonbounce* is a simple concept: if you send enough radio energy in the moon's direction, that old man moon will send some of it back to Mother Earth. This is high transmitting power and high-gain antenna territory; a very specialized mode of VHF and UHF communications. As specialized as EME is, however, packet radio EME experimentation has been conducted.

On June 29, 1986, W3IWI and Rich Strand, KL7RA, used an 85-foot antenna dish in Fairbanks, Alaska, to transmit approximately 700 kW EIRP at the moon on 432 MHz. After a 2.2-second Earth-to-moon and back-to-Earth signal delay, they successfully copied their own packet radio beacon. They also attempted to complete two-way contacts with stations in Mexico and Vancouver, Canada, but signals were too weak and fluttery to establish packet radio contacts.

CONCLUSION

Packet radio has entered outer space where its future may be enhanced by the successful use of space communications. Exciting times may be in store for packet radio space communicators because packet radio has the "right stuff."

14

Other Applications

In addition to the aforementioned applications, packet radio is being applied in a variety of other ways, too. This chapter will highlight some of these other applications.

APLink

APLink (for AMTOR/Packet Link) is a system developed by Vic Poor, W5SMM, that interfaces the VHF-UHF packet radio network with the HF AMTOR network. *APLink* system runs on IBM-PC/MS-DOS class computers.

To the user, the packet side looks like a PBBS, while the AMTOR side looks like a *mailbox* (*MBO*). Refer to the accompanying sidebar titled "*APLink* Packet User Command Set" for a list of the commands available on the packet side of the system.

The advantage of using *APLink* rather than a conventional VHF-UHF-HF packet radio system is that the nature of AMTOR allows it to work successfully under difficult HF radio conditions. Packet radio would have a hard time contending with those same HF radio conditions.

The disadvantage of using *APLink* is that all lowercase characters are converted to uppercase and all punctuation is converted to the closest available character because AMTOR only uses uppercase characters. As a result, the packet radio operator should choose his characters carefully when originating an *APLink* message. With that difference in mind, using *APLink* is very similar to using a PBBS and often the results are more successful.

APLink Packet User Command Set

The following commands are available with *APLink*, the AMTOR-packet mailbox/bulletin board written by Vic Poor, W5SMM. Note that there is no Kill command. Messages that have been read or forwarded are deleted automatically after 24 hours, whereas unread messages are deleted automatically after 21 days. Bulletins remain on the system until the originator or the SYSOP deletes them.

B—Log off the PBBS
CANCEL *n*—Cancels message number *n* if you originated the message
H—Displays description of each command
I—Displays Information about the system
L—Lists all messages on the system
L *n*—List messages numbered higher than *n*
L<—List messages from your station
L< *x*—List messages from station whose call sign is *x*
L>—List messages addressed to your station
L> *x*—List messages addressed to station whose call sign is *x*
LB—List all bulletin messages
LH—Lists all help files
LOGIN *x*—Logs you into the system using call sign *x*, which is different than the call sign that began the link
LR—Lists all users who have logged into the system in the last 24 hours
NTS—Lists all NTS messages that have not been forwarded from the system
R *n*—Read message numbered *n*
RN—Read all new messages addressed to you
SB *x*—Send a bulletin message whose subject is *x*
SB *x* @ *z*—Send a bulletin message whose subject is *x* via route *z*
SP *x*—Send message to station whose call sign is *x*
SP *x* @ *z*—Send a message to station whose call sign is *x* via route *z*
ST *x* @ *z*— Send NTS traffic to station whose call sign is *x* via route *z*
T—Rings bell at the SYSOP's terminal
V—Displays system version number

Awards

The ARRL issued plaques to the first 10 stations to achieve packet radio Worked All States (WAS) using direct (non-digipeater) contacts. The League continues to issue packet radio endorsements to the basic WAS award (packet radio WAS is not a separately numbered award).

Contests

Packet radio is also part of the Amateur Radio contest world. Two ARRL-sponsored contests include packet radio and more are sure to come as the popularity of the mode continues to grow.

Field Day

Since 1985, 100 bonus points are earned by completing at least one packet radio contact during the Field Day period. Digipeaters and network nodes can be used for the Field Day contact and each year, more and more Field Day stations include a TNC in their equipment array.

RTTY Roundup

In 1989, the ARRL began sponsoring the RTTY Roundup, a contest for the packet radio, RTTY, AMTOR and ASCII modes. The object of the contest is to work as many digital stations as you can worldwide. Your score equals the number of contacts multiplied by the number of different U.S. states, Canadian provinces and DXCC countries worked. Repeaters cannot be used to complete a contact. The popular contest is an annual event in early January.

Public Service Communications

Packet radio is a relative newcomer in Amateur Radio, but it has not taken long for packet public service applications to become obvious. In its short history, packet radio has provided communications in disasters, emergencies and for public events. Packet radio is also quickly becoming an integral cog in the National Traffic System machinery (refer to Chapter 9 for information on how to handle traffic via packet).

Emergency Communications

"Packet radio is a powerful tool for traffic handling, especially with detailed or lengthy text. Prepare and edit messages off line as text files. These can then be sent error free in just seconds, an important time-saver for busy traffic channels. Public service agencies are impressed by fast and accurate printed messages. Packet radio stations can even be mobile or portable. Relaying might be supplemented by AMTOR-Packet link (APLink), a system equipped to handle messages between AMTOR HF and packet radio VHF stations."

In 1984, the ARRL encouraged the use of packet radio by the Amateur Radio Emergency Service (ARES) when a 20-page chapter about packet radio communications was published in the ARRL's *Emergency Coordinator's Manual*. The quote above was taken from this book. The book was distributed to Emergency Coordinators across the United States and Canada. The ARRL further encouraged the use of packet radio in emergency and disaster field operations by making a 100-point bonus available for Field Day stations that used packet radio.

Since then, packet radio has been used to transfer traffic during the West Coast forest fires and earthquakes, Midwest floods and terrorist attacks and East Coast hurricanes and blizzards. Since packet radio stations can be portable, they are often set up at the site of a disaster to transfer messages back to packet radio stations set up at the state and private emergency agency headquarters. Government and private agencies involved with disasters and emergencies have been so impressed with the efficiency of amateur packet radio as a communications tool that they have provided funds for the purchase of packet radio equipment for their agency headquarters and field operations.

Amateurs already have plenty of experience using packet radio under fire. Some lessons have been learned and, as a result, some guidelines have been established. A set of such packet radio guidelines for emergencies and public service events was compiled by Patty Winter, N6BIS. An expanded version of those guidelines follows.

Planning

A thorough checklist should be prepared, including a list of the necessary TNC parameter settings for both the message-entry stations and portable digipeater stations (their parameters do differ).

Whenever possible, find out in advance what routes you will need to get traffic out of your operating location and what network nodes and digipeaters will be needed to support those routes. When selecting a route, use as few hops as possible to increase data transfer efficiency. If portable nodes or digipeaters are available, they may be placed on mountain tops to fill any gaps in the routes. If possible, test your routes with long files beforehand (long files tend to fail more often than short ones).

For a planned public-service event, all stations should be up and running at least one hour before the event begins. A realistic dry run, one to two weeks beforehand is very helpful in determining if there are any problems in the packet radio communications game plan.

Hardware Considerations

The packet radio station should have storage capability for data entry. Storage on disk is preferable to storing all your messages in computer volatile memory. In an emergency, power sources are often unreliable; if the data is not on disk, it will vaporize if the power goes off. If possible, power the packet radio station from an emergency power source to avoid commercial power line brownouts and blackouts.

If possible, two compatible computers should be used at the message-entry stations. Use one computer to enter and edit the messages and use the other computer for the actual packet radio transmissions. The computers should be compatible so that disks containing the information from the message entry computer can be transferred to the transmitting computer and used immediately (without requiring translation between incompatible computers).

A local PBBS can be very useful, if one is available or can be set up during the operation. The PBBS can be used to store and forward messages that are addressed out of the local area, or to store messages for stations that are not available when you need them. The object is to pass the traffic, and if you can pass it to a PBBS for later autoforwarding, so much the better.

One packet radio station in the emergency network should be connected to a printer to provide a written record of all of the traffic handled by the network. If more than one copy of the transcript is needed, use multiform (carbon) paper in the printer.

The use of standardized connectors provides flexibility when emergency equipment replacement is necessary. For example, many TNCs use the same type of connector for the radio (a 5-pin DIN-type connector), terminal (a 25-pin subminiature D-type connector) and power supply (a miniature phone plug). This means that many TNCs are interchangeable (check the wiring of the 5-pin DIN-type radio connection for incompatibility between certain TNCs).

Backup software and hardware (both computer and radio) should be available to counteract Murphy's Law. As anyone who has operated during Field Day or at an emergency can tell you, anything that can go wrong will!

Operating Procedures

There should be one packet radio net control station (NCS) if more than two packet radio stations are involved in the effort. If voice communications are used, a voice NCS should be appointed also. If there are two net-control stations (one for packet radio and one for voice), they should be located near each other so that they will be able to coordinate the nets more effectively and avoid duplication of efforts.

The packet radio NCS should establish the format, content and size of the packet radio messages. If every station cannot hear every other station, the NCS should quickly establish and announce a routing list showing what routes each station should use to communicate with the other stations.

The packet radio and voice NCSs should decide which mode will handle which traffic. Packet radio is best for large amounts of information, information requiring hard copy, complicated information with difficult spelling (names) or lots of numbers (addresses and telephone numbers) and information requiring some privacy or security. Voice communication is best for information that is tactical, uncomplicated and concise.

The message entry station should be set up for speed. Preprinted message forms should be used to eliminate the entry of repetitive information. All stations that are originating messages should use the same standard message format for quick collation of the information by the receiving stations.

The size of transmitted files should be short enough (approximately 50 lines) to ensure that the complete file will be sent before a disconnection occurs if the maximum number of retries is reached. The packets should be long enough, however, that each line of text does not force a new packet. If you send short (60 or 80-character) packets, you are wasting a lot of overhead (each packet's header and trailer).

Conclusion

The applications of packet radio are so varied that nearly every ham radio operator can satisfy his or her niche. If not, hams, more than anyone else, have the ability to construct their own packet radio niches. Witness the scratch-built niches described in this and the preceding chapters and you may be inspired to create your own niche.

Appendices

Section 4

Appendices—Commands, Control Characters, Messages, Sources and a Glossary for reference.

A

AX.25

The *AX.25 Amateur PacketRadio Link-Layer Protocol, Version 2.0*, commonly known as AX.25, was approved by the ARRL Board of Directors in October 1984. AX.25 is recognized by most packet radio operators as the *de facto* standard packet radio protocol. AX.25 specifies the content and format of an amateur packet radio frame and how that frame is handled at the *Link layer* by packet radio stations.

As defined, AX.25 works equally well in either *half-duplex* or *full-duplex* radio environments. It is designed to work with connections between individual packet radio stations or between an individual packet radio station and a *multiport controller*. AX.25 allows for *multiple connections* (if the packet radio device is capable of multiple connections), and the protocol does not prohibit a packet radio device from connecting with itself. The *Balanced Link Access Procedure (LAPB)* of *CCITT Recommendation X.25* was used as the model for AX.25, so the two protocols are similar. The primary differences are that AX.25 accommodates Amateur Radio call signs for the addressing of each transmitted packet and provides the ability for an unconnected station to send packets. This permits packet radio operators to send CQs, beacons and round-table transmissions.

AX.25 FRAMES AND FIELDS

AX.25 transmissions consist of small blocks of information called frames. There are three basic types of frames, the *Information frame* (or *I frame*), the *Supervisory*

FIELD:	FLAG	ADDRESS	CONTROL	FCS	FLAG
LENGTH:	8 BITS	112 - 560 BITS	8 BITS	16 BITS	8 BITS
CONTENTS:	01111110	CALL SIGNS & SSIDS OF DESTINATION, SOURCE, &, OPTIONALLY, DIGIPEATERS	FRAME TYPE	CALCULATED VALUE	01111110

FIRST BIT SENT — LAST BIT SENT

UNNUMBERED AND SUPERVISORY FRAMEs

FIELD:	FLAG	ADDRESS	CONTROL	PID	INFORMATION	FCS	FLAG
LENGTH:	8 BITS	112 - 560 BITS	8 BITS	8 BITS	N x 8 BITS	16 BITS	8 BITS
CONTENTS:	01111110	CALL SIGNS & SSIDS OF DESTINATION, SOURCE, &, OPTIONALLY, DIGIPEATERS	FRAME TYPE	LAYER 3 PROTOCOL TYPE	USER DATA	CALCULATED VALUE	01111110

FIRST BIT SENT — LAST BIT SENT

INFORMATION FRAME

Fig A-1—AX.25 unnumbered, supervisory and information frame formats.

frame (or *S frame*), and the *Unnumbered frame* (or *U frame*). An I frame contains the user data that is being transferred from one station to the other. An S frame provides control of the communications link. For example, S frames acknowledge the receipt of I frames or request the retransmission of I frames. U frames provide additional control of the communications link and also make it possible to send unconnected *Unnumbered Information* frames (*UI frames*).

A frame is subdivided into smaller blocks of information called *fields*. Each field is an integral length that is measured in *octets* (an octet is the equivalent of a *byte* or eight bits). Each frame contains a *flag field*, an *address field*, a *control field*, a *frame-check sequence field* and a final flag field. I frames and UI frames also include a *protocol identifier field* and an *information field*. (Figure A-1 shows the formats of the three basic frame types.)

The flag field indicates the beginning and end of a frame. One flag field may be shared by two frames; in such a situation, the single flag field indicates the end of the first frame and the beginning of the second frame. The flag field is one octet long and its contents are unique [01111110 (7E hexadecimal)] so that no other octet will be interpreted as a flag field.

A process called *zero bit insertion* or *bit stuffing* prevents the other octets between flag octets from having the same unique contents of the flag field. Whenever five consecutive one bits occur in the other octets (not flag octets) of a frame that is intended for transmission, the transmitting packet radio station inserts (or stuffs) a zero bit after the fifth one bit. Whenever five consecutive bits occur in a received frame, the receiving packet radio station discards the zero bit after the fifth one bit (to restore intelligence to the contents of the frame).

The address field contains the call signs of the source and destination of the frame. Optionally, it may also contain the call signs of one to eight digipeaters. The length of the address field varies from a minimum of 112 bits (14 octets) to a maximum of 560 bits (70 octets) depending on whether or not digipeaters are contained in the field and, if so, how many.

The first 7 octets of the address field contain the call sign and the *Secondary Station Identifier (SSID)* of the destination station. (The SSID permits one call sign to be used by more than one packet radio station. For example, the same call sign may be used by a digipeater station and the call-sign-holder's home station. The SSID may be a number from 0 to 15; if no SSID is specified, it is assumed to be 0.)

Octets 8 through 14 of the address field contain the call sign and SSID of the packet radio station that has originated the frame (the source station). If one or more digipeaters are specified for routing the frame, each digipeater's call sign and SSID is contained in the address field octets following the call sign and SSID of the source station (octets 16 through 70 maximum). Like the destination and source stations, the digipeater call sign and SSID are 7 octets in length. If more than one digipeater is contained in the address field, the first digipeater in the address field is the first digipeater in the specified route (the first one to retransmit the frame) and the last digipeater in the address field is the last digipeater in the specified route (the one that finally transmits the frame to the destination station).

The control field indicates the frame type. It is one octet long.

The protocol identifier field (or *PID field*) is only present in an I or UI frame and it indicates the type of network layer protocol that is in use, if any. The PID field is one octet long.

The information field contains the actual user data or intelligence that is transferred in an I, UI, or frame reject (FRMR) frame. The maximum length of an information field is 256 octets (prior to bit stuffing).

The frame check sequence (*FCS*) field is used for frame error checking. It contains a 16-bit number that is calculated from the transmitted data by the transmitting station according to *ISO 3309 (HDLC) Recommendations*. When the frame is received, the receiving station recalculates the FCS from the received data; if the contents of the FCS field are equal to the FCS calculated by the receiving station, the frame has been received without error. If the two are not equal, then the frame was received with an error and the receiving station discards the frame.

Supervisory Frames

Supervisory frames are used to control the communications link. The *Receive Not Ready (RNR)* frame indicates that the destination station is not able to accept any more I frames because of a temporary "busy" condition. The *Receive Ready (RR)* supervisory frame indicates that the destination station *is* able to receive more I frames (an RR clears an RNR condition). The RR and RNR frames may also acknowledge properly received I frames (frames where the received and recalculated FCSs are equal and the frames are in sequence). The *Reject (REJ)* supervisory frame is used by the destination station to request a retransmission when an out-of-sequence frame is received.

Unnumbered Frames

There are six types of Unnumbered frames. Five perform supervisory functions and the sixth permits stations to make unconnected transmissions.

The *Set Asynchronous Balanced Mode (SABM)* unnumbered frame initiates a connection between two packet radio stations, while the *Disconnect (DISC)* frame terminates a connection between two packet radio stations. The receipt and acceptance of an SABM or DISC frame is acknowledged by the *Unnumbered Acknowledge (UA)* frame. If the packet radio station is busy and unable to accept a connection at the moment, it rejects the SABM frame by transmitting a *Disconnected Mode (DM)* frame.

The *Frame Reject (FRMR)* frame indicates that the source station is unable to process a frame and that the error is such that resending the frame will not correct the problem. An FRMR is only sent when something abnormal occurs; it is rare.

The *Unnumbered Information (UI)* frame allows data to be transmitted from a source station without a connection to the destination station. Because there is no connection between a source station and destination station when a UI frame is sent, there is no end-to-end error-checking. This means that there is no guarantee that a UI frame will be received without error. UI frames are used for calling CQ, sending general announcements (beacons), in round-table discussions or any time error-free link-layer communication is not a requirement.

HOW AX.25 WORKS

WA1LOU wishes to connect with N1BKE, so WA1LOU commands his packet radio device to initiate the connection. (Typing *Connect N1BKE <CR>* at the command prompt does the trick.) In response, WA1LOU's terminal node controller (TNC) constructs a frame with "N1BKE0" in the destination address field and "WA1LOU0" in the source address field. The control field is set as an SABM frame. The SABM frame is transmitted to N1BKE-0 and the *acknowledgment timer (T1)* is started at WA1LOU. T1 is equal to at least twice the amount of time it takes to transmit the longest possible frame plus the amount of time it takes for the destination station to transmit the proper response frame. If one or more digipeaters are included in the route, T1 is increased accordingly.

If N1BKE-0 is monitoring the channel and is able to accept WA1LOU's request for a connection, N1BKE's TNC will respond to the SABM frame with a UA frame (WA1LOU's TNC will display **** CONNECTED to N1BKE-0*). If N1BKE is busy and unable to accept the connect request, the TNC will respond with a DM frame (WA1LOU's TNC will display **** N1BKE-0 busy* followed by **** DISCONNECTED*).

When WA1LOU receives N1BKE's response, the TNC cancels the T1 timer. If a UA frame was received, WA1LOU enters the data-transfer mode. If no response is received before T1 times out, WA1LOU continues to transmit SABM frames until a response is received or until the maximum number of retries permitted by WA1LOU's TNC is reached. (The TNC will display **** retry count exceeded* followed by **** DISCONNECTED*.)

In the data-transfer mode, WA1LOU transmits data to N1BKE. This data is transmitted by the TNC in the form of I frames. As each new I frame is transmitted, the T1 timer is started (or restarted, if it is already running) by the transmitting station. A maximum of seven I frames can be outstanding (unacknowledged) at one time.

If the destination station receives the I frame in the proper sequence and without error (the FCS checks out), the destination station sends an acknowledgment of reception. If the station has no I frames to send, it sends an RR frame (or RNR frame if it does not want to receive further I frames for the time being). If it has I frames to send, it can use the I frame to indicate the acknowledgment, or it can send an RR frame followed by the I frame.

If the destination station receives an I frame out of sequence, the frame is discarded and an REJ frame is transmitted. Out of sequence means that an I frame was received at the destination station in a different sequence than it was transmitted by the source station (as indicated by a difference between the received I frame's *send sequence number* and the destination station's *receive state variable*). When the sending station receives an REJ frame, it retransmits the rejected frame.

The destination station also discards an I frame if the frame's FCS does not match the calculated FCS. In this case, the destination station does not send an REJ, RR or RNR, so the source station's T1 timer runs out, which causes the source station to retransmit the frame and restart T1.

When the exchange of data between WA1LOU and N1BKE is completed, either station may initiate a disconnection. (This is done by entering the *Command Mode* and typing *Disconnect* at the command prompt.) In response, the TNC transmits a DISC frame to the other station and starts its T1 timer. The receiving station responds by sending a UA frame and entering the disconnected mode.

When the UA frame is received by the station initiating the disconnection, it cancels the T1 timer and enters the disconnected mode (The TNC will display *** *DISCONNECTED*). If no response is received before T1 times out, the station retransmits the DISC frame until a response is received, or until the maximum number of retries is reached. (The TNC will display *** *retry count exceeded* followed by *** *DISCONNECTED*.)

That's basically how AX.25 works! For full details concerning this protocol, *AX.25 Amateur Packet Radio Link-Layer Protocol, Version 2.0, October 1984* is available from ARRL headquarters.

B

TAPR TNC 2 Command Set

The following table lists the command set of the TAPR TNC 2, the mother of nearly every TNC in use today. The table includes the following information about each command: name, default setting, optional parameters and description of the function of the command. If default and selectable parameters are not listed, then the command is an immediate command; otherwise, it is a configuration command. Each table is subdivided into the various command categories: character, identification, link, monitor, reinitialization, serial port and timing commands.

Character Commands

Command	Default	Parameters	Description
BKondel *x*	ON	ON/OFf	Selects how deletions are displayed by terminal.
CANline *n*	$18 <CTRL-X>	0-$7F	Selects cancel line input control character.
CANPac *n*	$19 <CTRL-Y)	0-$7F	Selects cancel packet input control character.
COMmand *n*	$03 <CTRL-C>	0-$7F	Selects Command Mode entry control character.
DELete *x*	OFf	ON/OFf	Selects delete input editing control character ($7F or $08).
PASs *n*	$16 <CTRL-V>	0-$7F	Selects pass input editing command control character.
REDispla *n*	$12 <CTRL-R>	0-$7F	Selects redisplay-line input editing control character.
SEndpac *n*	$0D <CR>	0-$7F	Selects Converse Mode control character that force packet transmissions.
STArt *n*	$11 <CTRL-Q>	0-$7F	Selects restart control character for TNC output to terminal.
STOp *n*	$13 <CTRL-S>	0-$7F	Selects stop control character for TNC output to terminal.
STReamsw *n*	$7C |	0-$FF	Selects character that indicates new stream.
XOff *n*	$13 <CTRL-S>	0-$7F	Selects the stop control character for terminal output to TNC.
XON *n*	$11 <CTRL-Q>	0-$7F	Selects restart control character for terminal output to TNC.

Identification Commands

Command	Default	Parameters	Description
Beacon *x*	Every 0	Every/After 0-250 (× 10 sec)	Enables/disables beacon transmissions
BText *n*	none	0-128 ASCII characters	Enters contents of beacon.
CMSg *x*	OFf	ON/OFf	Enables/disables CTEXT message transmission after connection.
CText *n*	none	0 -120 ASCII characters	Enters contents of packet sent after a connection.
HId *x*	OFf	ON/OFf	Enables/disables HDLC identification by digital repeater.
Id	-	-	Transmits special identification packet.
MYAlias *x*	none	call sign [and optionally SSID (0-15)]	Enters alternate call sign (and optionally SSID).
MYcall *x*	NOCALL-0	call sign [and optionally SSID (0-15)]	Enters call sign (and optionally SSID).
Unproto *x*	CQ	call sign (Via callsign1,... callsign 8)	Selects unprotocol mode packet destination (optionally, via callsign1,... callsign8).

Link Commands

Command	*Default*	*Parameters*	*Description*
ACkprior *x*	ON	ON/OFf	Enables/disables prioritized acknowledgments.
Ax25l2v2 *x*	ON	ON/OFf	Selects Version 2.0 or 1.0 of AX.25 Level 2.
CALibra	-	-	Transfers to modem Calibration Mode.
CHECKV1 *x*	OFf	ON/OFf	Enables/disables automatic disconnections in AX.25 Level 2, Version 1 links when CHeck time expires.
CMSGDisc *x*	OFf	ON/OFf	Enables/disables automatic disconnection after connection.
CONMode *x*	Convers	Convers/Trans	Selects automatic entry into Converse or Transparent Mode after connection.
Connect *x*	-	call sign (Via callsign1,... callsign8)	Initiates connection to call sign (optionally, via callsign1,... callsign8).
CONOk *x*	ON	ON/OFf	Accepts/rejects connect requests.
CONPerm *x*	OFf	ON/OFf	Enables/disables maintenance of current connection.
CONVers	-	-	Transfers from Command Mode to Converse Mode.
CR *x*	ON	ON/OFf	Enables/disables adding send-packet character to Converse Mode packets.
DIGipeat *x*	ON	ON/OFf	Enables/disables repeater function of the TNC.
Disconne	-	-	Initiates disconnection from connected station.
FIRMRnr *x*	ON	ON/OFf	Enables/disables the stop sending of data when an RNR frame is received.
FUlldup *x*	OFf	ON/OFf	Enables/disables full duplex mode.
LFadd *x*	OFf	ON/OFf	Enables/disables adding <LF> after each <CR> in outgoing packets.
MAXframe *n*	4	1-7 (packets)	Selects maximum number of outstanding unacknowledged packets.
NEwmode *x*	OFf	ON/OFf	Enables/disables automatic transfer to Command Mode after disconnection.
NOmode *x*	ON	ON/OFf	Enables/disables manual-only mode transfers.
Paclen *n*	128	0-255 (bytes) (0 = 256)	Selects number of bytes per packet that automatically force a packet transmissions.
PASSAll *x*	OFf	ON/OFf	Enables/disables accepting packets with invalid CRCs.
RECOnnect *x*	-	call sign (Via callsign1,... callsign8)	Initiates reconnection with currently connected station via different path.
REtry *n*	10	0-15 (packets)	Selects maximum number of times unacknowledged frames are retransmitted.
RXCAL	-	-	Transfers to demodulator alignment mode.
SLots *n*	0-127	3	Selects number of slots from which to choose when accessing a channel.
TRACe *x*	OFf	ON/OFf	Enables/disables Trace Mode.
Trans	-	-	Transfers from Command Mode to Transparent Mode.
TXUIfram *x*	OFf	ON/OFf	Enables/disables sending unconnected information frames except for Beacon and ID frames.
USers *n*	1	0-10 (connections)	Selects number of active requested connections that may be established.

Monitor Commands

Command	*Default*	*Parameters*	*Description*
XMitok *x*	ON	ON/OFf	Enables/disables transmitting.
BBSmsgs *x*	OFf	ON/OFf	Controls how certain messages are displayed in Command and Converse Modes.
BUdlist *x*	OFf	ON/OFf	Ignores frames from stations listed/not listed by LCALLS command.
CBell *x*	OFf	ON/OFf	Enables/disables <BELL> when connection is established.
CONStamp *x*	OFf	ON/OFf	Enables/disables connect status message time stamping.
CStatus	-	-	Displays stream identifier and link state of the streams.
DAytime *n*	none	yymmddhhmm (date and time)	Sets TNC clock.
DAYUsa *x*	ON	ON/OFf	Selects mm/dd/yy or dd-mm-yy format for display of dates.
DISPlay *x*	-	(optionally A, C, H, I, L, M, T)	Displays status of TNC parameters.
HEaderln *x*	OFf	ON/OFf	Selects printing packets and headers on same line or on separate lines.
HEALled *x*	OFf	ON/OFf	Enables/disables random flashing of CON and STA front panel indicators.
LCAlls *x*	none	callsign1,... callsign8	Enters call signs monitored or not monitored via BUDLIST command.
MAll *x*	ON	ON/OFf	Selects monitoring connected and unconnected or only unconnected packets.
MCOM *x*	OFf	ON/OFf	Enables/disables monitoring connect and disconnect frames via MONITOR command.
MCon *x*	ON	ON/OFf	Enables/disables monitoring while the TNC is connected.
MFilter *n1...n4*	none	0-$7F	Select 1 to 4 ASCII characters to be stripped from monitored packets.
MHClear	-	-	Clears list of stations heard by the TNC.
MHeard	-	-	Displays list of stations heard by TNC since last time the MHClear command was invoked.
MNonax25 *x*	OFf	ON/OFf	Enables/disables the filtering of level 3 and 4 networking frames.
Monitor *x*	ON	ON/OFf	Enables/disables packet monitoring.
MRpt *x*	ON	ON/OFf	Enables/disables display of digital repeater call signs for monitored packets.
MStamp *x*	OFf	ON/OFf	Enables/disables monitored frame time-stamping.
STATUS	-	-	Displays status of the current outgoing packet link buffer.
STREAMCa *x*	OFf	ON/OFf	Enables/disables displaying call sign of the connected station after stream identifier.
STREAMDbl *x*	OFf	ON/OFf	Enables/disables displaying two streamswitch characters for each one received.
TRIes *n*	none	0-15 (retries)	Displays or enters the number of retries of currently selected stream.

Reinitialization Commands

Command	*Default*	*Parameters*	*Description*
RESET	-	-	Reinitializes TNC and resets TNC parameters to default values.
RESTART	-	-	Reinitializes TNC using the TNC parameter values stored in RAM.

Serial Port Commands

Command	*Default*	*Parameters*	*Description*
8bitconv *x*	OFf	ON/OFf	Strips/passes eighth bit in Converse Mode.
AUtolf *x*	ON	ON/OFf	Enables/disables automatic <LF> sending after each <CR>.
AWlen *n*	7	7-8 (bits)	Selects number of data bits per word.
Echo *x*	ON	ON/OFf	Enables/disables terminal character echo.
EScape *x*	OFf	ON/OFf	Selects $ or <ESCAPE> as escape character sent to terminal from TNC.
Flow *x*	ON	ON/OFf	Enables/disables type-in flow control.
KIss *x*	OFf	ON/OFf	Enables/disables the Serial Line Interface Protocol (SLIP) between TNC and computer.
LCok *x*	ON	ON/OFf	Disables/Enables translation of lowercase characters to uppercase.
LCStream *x*	ON	ON/OFf	Enables/disables uppercase conversion of character following streamswitch.
LFIgnore *x*	OFf	ON/OFf	Enables/disables lack of response of TNC to <LF> in Command and Converse Modes.
NUcr *x*	OFf	ON/OFf	Enables/disables sending <NULL> characters to terminal after each <CR>.
NULf *x*	OFf	ON/OFf	Enables/disables sending <NULL> characters to terminal after each <LF>.
NULLs *n*	0	0-30 (<NULL> characters)	Selects number of <NULL> characters to be sent via NUCR and NULF commands.
PARity *n*	3	0,1,2,3 (= none, odd, no, even parity)	Selects terminal parity.
RXBlock *x*	OFf	ON/OFf	Enables/disables sending data to terminal in RXBLOCK format.
Screenln *n*	80	0-255 (columns)	Selects number of columns per line to be displayed by terminal.
TRFlow *x*	OFf	ON/OFf	Enables/disables terminal software flow control in Transparent Mode.
TXFlow *x*	OFf	ON/OFf	Enables/disables TNC software flow control in Transparent Mode.
Xflow *x*	ON	ON/OFf	Selects XON/XOFF or hardware (RTS) flow control.

Timing Commands

Command	*Default*	*Parameters*	*Description*
ACKTime *n*	14	0-250 (× 10 ms)	Selects delay between receiving an I frame and sending an acknowledgment.
AXDelay *n*	0	0-180 (× 10 ms)	Selects delay between keying voice repeater and sending data.
AXHang *n*	0	0-20 (× 100 ms)	Selects voice repeater hang time.
CALSet *n*	2060	0-65535	Selects count setting used for modem calibration.
CHeck *n*	30	0-250 (× 10 sec)	Selects connection inactivity time-out.
CLKADJ *n*	0	0-65535	Selects correction factor for TNC clock.
CMdtime *n*	1	0-250 (sec)	Selects Transparent Mode time-out.
CPactime *x*	OFf	ON/OFf	Enables/disables periodic automatic packet transmission in Converse Mode.
DEAdtime *n*	33	0-250 (× 10 ms)	Selects time it takes local receiver to detect remote transmitter keying-up.
DWait *n*	16	0-250 (× 10 ms)	Selects transmission delay (to avoid collisions).
FRack *n*	3	1 -15 (sec)	Selects frame acknowledgment time-out.
PACTime *x*	After 10	Every/After 0-250 (× 100 ms)	Selects packet time-out.
RESptime *n*	5	0-250 (× 100 ms)	Selects minimum delay for acknowledgment packet transmissions.
TXdelay *n*	30	0-120 (× 10 ms)	Selects delay between keying transmitter and sending data.
TXDELAYC *n*	2	0-120	Selects additional delay between keying transmitter and sending data.

C

TAPR TNC 2 Control Characters

Control characters are keyboard characters that you type to control certain TNC functions. You enter most control characters by typing a specific letter while pressing your keyboard's control key. For example, to enter <CTRL-C>, you type the letter C while pressing the control key. | and <CR> are exceptions. You enter | by pressing the | key and you enter <CR> by pressing the Return (or Carriage Return) key.

ASCII	***Hex***	***Dec***	***Command***	***Function***
|	7C	124	STReamsw	Indicates a new stream.
<CR>	0D	13	SEndpac	Sends a packet in the Converse Mode.
<CTRL-C>	03	3	COMmand	Transfers from Converse to Command Mode.
<CTRL-H>	08	8	BKondel	Display indication of a character deletion.
<CTRL-H>	08	8	DELete	Deletes a character.
<CTRL-Q>	11	17	STArt	Restarts TNC output to terminal.
<CTRL-Q>	11	17	XON	Restarts terminal output to TNC.
<CTRL-R>	12	18	REDisplay	Redisplays currently typed line.
<CTRL-S>	13	19	STOp	Stops TNC output to terminal.
<CTRL-S>	13	19	XOff	Stops terminal output to TNC.
<CTRL-V>	16	22	PASs	Includes following character in a packet.
<CTRL-X>	18	24	CANline	Cancels currently typed line.
<CTRL-Y>	19	25	CANPac	Cancels currently entered packet.

D

TAPR TNC 2 Messages

This appendix describes each status message that may be sent to a terminal by a TAPR TNC 2 (or clone).

bbRAM loaded with defaults—Indicates that RAM was loaded with default parameter values.

cmd:—Command Mode command prompt; indicates that the TNC is waiting for a command.

FRMR sent: n—Indicates that a protocol error occurred during a connection and a FRMR packet was transmitted to the remote TNC to synchronize frame numbers; the FRMR packet contains three bytes in its information frame represented in hexadecimal by *n*.

FRMR rcvd:—Indicates that a protocol error occurred during a connection and that a FRMR packet was received from the remote TNC.

Link state is: CONNECT in progress—Indicates that the Connect command was invoked while the TNC was already attempting a connection.

Link state is: CONNECTED to x (*VIA* x1,x2... x8)—Indicates that the Connect command was invoked while the TNC was already connected to station *x* [optionally, VIA digipeater(s) *x1* through *x8*].

Link state is: DISCONNECT in progress—Indicates that the Disconnect command or the Connect command without options was invoked while the TNC was attempting a disconnection.

Link state is: DISCONNECTED—Indicates that the Disconnect command or the Connect command without options was invoked while the TNC was disconnected.

Link state is: FRMR in progress—Indicates that a protocol error occurred during a connection.

too many packets outstanding—Indicates that the Converse or Transparent command was invoked before a sufficient number of the outstanding packets were acknowledged.

was—Indicates the previous value of a configurable parameter after a command is invoked to change that value.

*** *connect request:* x (*VIA* x1,x2... x8)—Indicates that the TNC has rejected a connect request from station *x* [optionally, VIA digipeater(s) *x1* through *x8*].

*** *CONNECTED to:* x (*VIA* x1,x2... x8)—Indicates that a connection occurred between the TNC and station *x* [optionally, VIA digipeater(s) *x1* through *x8*].

*** *DISCONNECTED*—Indicates that a disconnection occurred.

*** *LINK OUT OF ORDER, possible data loss*—Indicates that a link failure has occurred with the Conperm parameter enabled.

*** *retry count exceeded*

*** *DISCONNECTED*—Indicates that a disconnection occurred because the allowed number of retries was exceeded.

*** x *busy*

*** *DISCONNECTED*—Indicates that a connect request was rejected by station whose call sign is *x*.

?already connected to that station—In multiple connection operation, indicates that the Connect command was invoked to attempt a connection to a station that was already connected to the TNC.

?bad—Indicates that an entry could not be interpreted by the TNC as a parameter of the invoked command.

?call—Indicates that an entry could not be interpreted as a call sign by the TNC.

?clock not set—After the Daytime command is invoked, indicates that the clock has not been set.

?EH—Indicates that an entry could not be interpreted as a command by the TNC.

?not enough—Indicates that an insufficient number of parameters were specified for the invoked command.

?not while connected—Indicates that an attempt was made to change the Mycall or AX25L2V2 parameter while connected or while attempting a connection.

?not while disconnected—Indicates that an attempt was made to invoke a command that can only be used during a connection.

?range—Indicates that the value specified in a command was not an acceptable value.

?too long—Indicates that an invoked command contained too many characters.

?too many—Indicates that too many parameters were specified for the invoked command.

?VIA—Indicates that VIA was not used when invoking a command that specified digipeater call sign(s).

IA

Tucson Amateur Packet Radio

TNC 2 AX.25 Level 2

Version 2.0 Release x.x.x *Checksum* $x

cmd:—Displayed after you turn on or reset the TNC; *x.x.x* indicates the revision level of the TNC firmware and *x* indicates the TNC firmware checksum.

E

Sources

The following listings represent sources of packet radio products (hardware and software, commercial and noncommercial) and packet radio organizations.

HARDWARE AND SOFTWARE SUPPLIERS

The parentheses after each listing contain the type of hardware and/or software offered by the supplier, according to the following legend:

1—TNC hardware
2—TNC software
3—terminal software
4—modem hardware
5—modem software
6—PBBS software
7—network hardware
8—network software
9—other hardware
10—other software

Advanced Electronic Applications, Inc (AEA)—see Timewave Technology

Alinco Electronics Inc, 438 Amapola Ave, #130, Torrance, CA 90501, phone 310-618-8616, FAX 310-618-8758 (9)

Azden Communications Division, 147 New Hyde Park Rd, Franklin Sq, NY 11010, phone 516-328-7501, FAX 516-328-7506 (9)

Bob Bruninga, WB4APR, 115 Old Farm Ct, Glen Burnie, MD 21061 (10)

CompuServe, 5000 Arlington Centre Blvd, Columbus, OH 43220 (2, 3, 5, 6, 8, 10)

Larry East, W1HUE, 1355 Rimline Dr, Idaho Falls, ID 83401 (3)

Electrosoft, 1656 S California St, Loveland, CO 80537 (3)

Roy Engehausen, AA4RE, 8660 Del Rey Ct, Gilroy, CA 95020 (6)

Jim Flannery, KØUNX, 8098 S Carr Ct, Littleton, CO 80123 (3)

Georgia Radio Amateur Packet Enthusiast Society (GRAPES), PO Box 871, Alpharetta, GA 30239-0871 (4)

Monty Haley, WJ5W, Rte 1, Box 210b, Evening Shade, AR 72532 (3, 6)

Hamilton and Area Packet Network (HAPN), 5193 Whitechurch Rd, Mt. Hope, ON L0R 1W0, Canada, phone 905-692-3802 (1, 2, 3)

InterFlex Systems Design Group, PO Box 6418, Laguna Niguel, CA 92607-6418, phone 714-496-6639, FAX 714-496-8041 (3)

Jeff Jacobsen, WA7MBL, 1400 E 900 N, Logan, UT 84341 (6)

Kantronics, 1202 E 23rd St, Lawrence, KS 66046-5006, phone 913-842-7745, FAX 913-842-2031 (1, 3, 4, 7, 9)

MFJ Enterprises Inc, PO Box 494, Mississippi State, MS 39762, phone 601-323-5869, FAX 601-323-6551 (1, 3, 4, 9)

Weo Moerner, WN6I, 8720 Cliffridge Ave, La Jolla, CA 92037 (6)

Ottawa Amateur Radio Club, Packet Working Group, PO Box 8873, Ottawa, ON K1G 3J2, Canada, e-mail bm@hydra.carelton.ca (4, 8)

PacComm Packet Radio Systems, Inc, 4413 N Hesperides St, Tampa, FL 33614-7618, phone 813-874-2980, FAX 813-872-8696, e-mail sales@paccomm.com (1, 2, 3, 4, 7, 8, 9, 10)

David Palmer, N6KL, 7628 Estate Cir., Longmont, CO 80503 (6)

Pavilion Software, PO Box 803, Amherst, NH 03031 (10)

Mike Pechura, WA8BXN, 10809 Beechwood Dr, Kirtland, OH 44094 (6)

Vic Poor, W5SMM, 1208 E River Dr. 302, Melbourne, FL 32901 (10)

Radio Amateur Telecommunications Society (RATS), 206 North Vivyen St, Bergenfield, NJ 07621 (6, 8)

Ron Raikes, WA8DED, 9211 Pico Vista Rd, Downey, CA 90240 (2, 8)

Sigma Design Associates, PO Box 49085, Colorado Springs, CO 80949-9085, phone 719-260-5513 (evenings), e-mail 70611.1340@compuserve.com (2, 3, 4, 5)

Tekk, Inc, 226 Northwest Pkwy, Kansas City, MO 64150, phone 1-800-521-8355, 816-746-1098, FAX 816-746-1093 (9)

Texas Packet Radio Society, Inc, PO Box 50238, Denton, TX 76206-0238 (3, 7, 8)

Tigertronics, Inc., 400 Daily Ln., PO Box 5210, Grants Pass, OR 97527, phone 1-800-822-9722 or 503-474-6700, FAX 503-474-6703 (2, 3, 4)

Timewave Technology, Inc., 1301 Corporate Center Dr, Suite 140, St Paul, MN 55121, phone 612-452-5939, FAX 612-452-4571, e-mail sales@timewave.com (1, 3, 4, 9)

Tucson Amateur Packet Radio Corporation (TAPR), 8987-309 E Tanque Verde Rd, Tucson, AZ 85749-9399, phone 817-383-0000, FAX 817-566-2544 (2, 3, 4, 5, 6, 8, 9, 10)

ORGANIZATIONS

Organizational periodicals, if any, follow the organization address.

The Amateur Radio Research and Development Corp (AMRAD), PO Drawer 6148, McLean, VA 22106-6148, *The AMRAD Newsletter*

American Radio Relay League (ARRL), 225 Main St, Newington, CT 06111, *QST, QEX*

AMSAT-NA, The Radio Amateur Satellite Corp, 850 Sligo Ave, Silver Spring, MD 20910-4702, *The AMSAT Journal*

Chicago Area Packet Radio Association (CAPRA), PO Box 8251, Rolling Meadows, IL 60008, *The CAPRA Beacon*

Georgia Radio Amateur Packet Enthusiast Society (GRAPES), PO Box 871, Alpharetta, GA 30239-0871, *Grapevine*

Hamilton and Area Packet Network (HAPN), 5193 Whitechurch Rd, Mt Hope, ON L0R 1W0, Canada

Northern California Packet Association (NCPA), PO Box 61716, Sunnyvale, CA 94088-1761, *NCPA Downlink*

Northwest Amateur Packet Radio Association (NAPRA), PO Box 70405, Bellevue, WA 98007, *Dedicated Link*

Ottawa Amateur Radio Club, Packet Working Group, PO Box 8873, Ottawa, ON K1G 3J2, Canada

Radio Amateur Telecommunications Society (RATS), 206 North Vivyen St, Bergenfield, NJ 07621

Southern California Digital Communications Council (SCDCC), PO Box 2744-1307, Huntington Beach, CA 92647, *I-Frame*

Texas Packet Radio Society, Inc, PO Box 50238, Denton, TX 76206-0238, *The TPRS Quarterly Report*

Tucson Amateur Packet Radio Corporation (TAPR), 8987-309 E Tanque Verde Rd, Tucson, AZ 85749-9399, *Packet Status Register*

F

Glossary of Terms

<CR>—abbreviation for carriage return

acknowledgment timer—the AX.25 timer that causes the TNC to interrogate the linked TNC when a packet is not acknowledged before the timer expires; also called the T1 timer

Address Resolution Protocol (ARP)—part of the TCP/IP suite of protocols that provides the datagram address format required by the Internet Protocol

address—the identification of a packet source or destination

address field—the field in an AX.25 frame containing the call signs of the source and destination of the frame and, optionally, the call signs of one to eight digipeaters

AFSK—abbreviation for audio-frequency-shift keying

amateur X.25 (AX.25)—the link-layer packet radio protocol based on the CCITT X.25 packet-switching protocol

American National Standard Code for Information Interchange (ASCII)—a seven bit digital code used in computer and radioteleprinter applications

ampr.org—the amateur TCP/IP packet radio Internet domain

AMPRNET—the ARPANET name assignment for the amateur packet radio TCP/IP network

AMSAT—abbreviation for The Radio Amateur Satellite Corporation

APLink—a system that interfaces the VHF and UHF packet radio network with the HF AMTOR network

APRS—abbreviation for *Automatic Packet Reporting System*

ARP—abbreviation for Address Resolution Protocol

ARPANET—an early long distance packet switching hard-wired network that was developed under the Defense Advanced Projects Research Agency (DARPA, formerly ARPA)

The ARRL Repeater Directory—an annual ARRL publication that lists packet radio digipeaters, network nodes, gateways, BBS, etc, by state or province

ASCII—abbreviation for American National Standard Code for Information Interchange

asynchronous—a data transmission timing technique that adds extra bits of information to indicate the beginning and end of each transmitted character

audio-frequency-shift keying (AFSK)—a method of transmitting digital information by switching between two audio tones fed into the transmitter audio input

autobaud—the ability of a communications device to automatically adapt to whatever data rate is used by the terminal connected to it

Automatic Packet Reporting System (APRS)—a packet radio application for tracking real-time events by graphically displaying information on maps displayed on the user's computer screen

automatic line feed—a DTE or DCE (TNC) function that causes a line feed control character to be sent whenever a carriage return control character is sent

AX.25—the link-layer packet radio protocol based on the CCITT X.25 packet-switching protocol

backbone—the part of a packet radio network that is used strictly for the transfers of data; it has limited or no user access

backspace—a DTE key or a control character that deletes previously typed characters

Balanced Link Access Procedure (LAPB)—the CCITT X.25 link-layer protocol that was the model for AX.25

battery-backed RAM (bbRAM)—RAM that is powered by a battery to enable it to store data while its host device is turned off

baud—a unit of signalling speed equal to one pulse (event or symbol) per second in a single-channel transmission

bbRAM—abbreviation for battery-backed RAM

BBS—abbreviation for bulletin-board system

beacon—a TNC function that permits a station to automatically send unconnected packets at regular intervals

beacon after mode—beacon transmissions that only occur when the channel is clear and has not been in use for some time

Bell 103—the designation for the modem standard that transfers data at 300 bauds using 200 Hz frequency-shift-keyed tones at 1170 and 2125 Hz; commonly used for HF packet applications

Bell 202—the designation for the modem standard that transfers data at 1200 bauds using frequency-shift-keyed tones at 1200 and 2200 Hz; commonly used for VHF packet applications *binary*—the base two number system that uses the numerals 0 and 1

bit—binary digit, a signal that is either on/one or off/zero; bits are combined to represent alphanumeric and control characters for data communications

bit rate—the speed at which information is transferred, usually expressed in bauds or bits per second; also called data rate

bit stuffing—a process that prevents AX.25 fields from having the same unique contents of the flag field; also called zero bit insertion

bit/s—abbreviation for bits per second

bits per character—the number of bits that are combined to represent alphanumeric and control characters for data communications

bits per second (bit/s)—a measure of the speed at which information is transferred

buffer—a portion of computer memory that is set aside to temporarily store data that is being received or transmitted

bulletin-board system (BBS)—a computer system where messages and files can be stored for other users

byte—a group of bits, usually eight in number

calling frequency—an operating frequency that is used only for establishing communications; once communications have been established on the calling frequency, the operators switch to a less-used frequency

carriage return (<CR>)—a DTE key or a control character that is used to indicate the end of a line of typed information; it causes the DTE display to begin printing at the left-hand margin

carrier—an electromagnetic wave that may be varied in order to transmit information

CCITT—abbreviation for International Telegraph and Telephone Consultative Committee

character bits—the bits that represent an alphanumeric or control character

checksum—check summation; the sum (in hexadecimal) of the bits in the TNC software in ROM; it should be equal to the checksum published in the TNC manual

clone—a device that duplicates another device

collision—a condition that occurs when two or more packet radio transmissions occur at the same time; when a collision occurs, neither packet reaches its destination

command mode—the TNC operating mode where the TNC is waiting for command input from the user

command mode character—a control character that causes the TNC to enter the command mode

configuration command—a TNC command that selects a parameter that is used by the TNC when it performs a task

connect—to establish a communications link (a connection) between two packet radio stations

connection protocol—a Network layer protocol that sets up and maintains a clearly defined path for the transfer of packets between the source and destination during a single data communications session; also called virtual circuit protocol

connectionless protocol—a Network layer protocol that transfers each packet independently along the best available route; also called datagram protocol

control field—the field in an AX.25 frame that indicates the frame type

converse mode—the TNC operating mode where the TNC is transferring data to and from the user

data circuit-terminating equipment, data communications equipment (DCE)—the device that provides communications between a DTE and radio equipment or telephone lines

data communications software—a computer program that causes a computer to function as a DTE for the purpose of transferring data over a communications medium

data rate—the speed at which information is transferred, usually expressed in bauds or bits per second; also called bit rate

data terminal equipment (DTE)—a device that is used as an interface between a human and a computer to allow the human to exchange information with the computer

datagram—a Network layer protocol that transfers each packet independently along the best available route; also called connectionless protocol

DCE—abbreviation for data circuit-terminating equipment and data communications equipment

default—the state of a TNC parameter after the TNC is initially turned on or reset

demodulate—the process of retrieving information from a modulated carrier

destination—the intended recipient of a packet frame

deviation—the shift or change of carrier frequency that encodes amplitude in an FM signal

digipeater—digital repeater, a device that receives, temporarily stores and then transmits (repeats) packet radio transmissions that are specifically addressed for routing through the digipeater

digital signal processing (DSP)—a software technology that emulates hardware, such as modems and filters, in software

DISC—abbreviation for Disconnect frame

Disconnect frame (DISC)—an AX.25 unnumbered frame that terminates a connection

Disconnected Mode frame (DM)—an AX.25 unnumbered frame that indicates the rejection of a Set Asynchronous Balanced Mode frame

DM—abbreviation for Disconnected Mode frame

domain—a subsection of the Internet

Doppler shift—the change in frequency that occurs as a transmitter in an orbiting satellite moves in relationship to a stationary ground station receiver

download—to receive files from a PBBS or other packet radio station

DSP—abbreviation for digital signal processing

DTE—abbreviation for data terminal equipment

dumb terminal—a simple DTE that provides only basic input and output functions

duplex—a mode of communications where you transmit on one frequency and receive on another

Earth-to-moon-to-Earth (EME)—mode of communications in which VHF and UHF signals are reflected off the moon; also called moonbounce *echo*—a DTE and DCE (TNC) function that prints each character typed at the DTE keyboard on the display

EIA—abbreviation for Electronic Industries Association

EIA-232—the EIA standard for DTE-to-DCE (TNC) interfacing that specifies the interface signals and their electrical characteristics

Electronic Industries Association (EIA)—an organization composed of representatives of the United States electronics industry; the EIA is involved in formulating data communication standards.

EME—abbreviation for Earth-to-moon-to-Earth

emulate—to mimic; often used to describe software that attempts to perform the function of hardware

end-to-end acknowledgment—the networking protocol in which only the destination station or node informs the originating station or node that it has received a packet correctly

ENTER—a key on a computer keyboard that causes the computer to accept the information previously typed at its keyboard

enter—to use a key (for example, the ENTER key) on a computer keyboard to cause the computer to accept the information previously typed at its keyboard

EPROM—abbreviation for erasable programmable ROM

erasable programmable ROM—read-only memory whose contents can be deleted (by ultraviolet light) and replaced

escape—a sequence of alphanumeric characters that are typed at a DTE keyboard to cause the DCE (TNC) to exit the current operating mode and return to the previous operating mode

FCS—abbreviation for frame check sequence

field—a subdivision of an AX.25 frame

File Transport Protocol (FTP)—part of the TCP/IP suite of protocols that allows the user to transfer files to or from the computer at another node

FINGER—part of the TCP/IP suite of protocols that allows a station to obtain information about any TCP/IP station that is on the air

flag field—the field in an AX.25 frame that indicates the beginning and end of a frame

flow control—the stopping and restarting of the transfer of characters between the DTE and a DCE (TNC)

Frame Reject frame (FRMR)—an AX.25 unnumbered frame that indicates that the source station is unable to process a frame and that the error is such that resending the frame will not correct the problem

frame—a group of AX.25 fields consisting of an opening flag, address, control, information, frame-check-sequence and ending flag fields

frame check sequence field—the field in an AX.25 frame that is used for frame error checking

frame-check sequence (FCS)—a calculated number contained in each packet frame that is used by the receiving station to determine the integrity of the frame

frequency-shift keying (FSK)—a method of transmitting digital information by switching an RF carrier between two separate frequencies

FRMR—abbreviation for Frame Reject frame

FSK—abbreviation for frequency-shift keying

FTP—abbreviation for File Transport Protocol

full-duplex—a communications mode where it is possible to transmit and receive simultaneously

G3RUH modem—a 9600-bit/s packet radio modem

gateway—a device or PBBS function that (1) allows packet radio stations on different operating frequencies to communicate with each other or (2) allows packet radio stations to communicate via the Internet

Global Positioning System (GPS)—a system that uses orbiting satellites to determine the location of GPS receiving stations on the surface of the Earth

GPS—abbreviation for Global Positioning System

half-duplex—a communications mode where you alternately transmit and receive

hang time—the transmission of an unmodulated carrier by a voice repeater after each transmission to indicate that the repeater is functioning; also called squelch tail

hardware flow control—flow control that is controlled by signals from the DCE (TNC) and DTE on the serial interface between the two devices

header—the non-data portion of a packet frame; the header precedes the data portion of the frame

hexadecimal—the base-16 numbering system that uses the numerals 0 through 9 and letters A through F

hidden transmitter—a packet radio station that can be heard by only one of two other stations that are connected; in such a situation, two stations that cannot hear each other may transmit simultaneously, which results in the reception of interference or a packet collision by a third station

hierarchical address—an addressing scheme for packet radio mail composed of the call sign, home PBBS, geographical region, country and continent of the addressed station

home PBBS—the PBBS where a station receives packet radio messages

host— each computer at each packet radio station in the TCP/IP network

I frame—abbreviation for information frame

immediate command—a command that causes the TNC to perform a task immediately

Information frame (I frame)—an AX.25 frame that contains user data

information field—the field in an AX.25 frame that contains the user data

information transfer rate—the number of equivalent binary digits transferred per second

intelligent terminal—a DTE that provides numerous support functions as well as basic input and output functions

International Telegraph and Telephone Consultative Committee (CCITT)—an International Telecommunication Union agency involved in formulating international data communication standards

Internet Protocol (IP)—part of the TCP/IP suite of protocols that tracks the network node addresses, routes outgoing packets and recognizes received packets

IP—abbreviation for Internet Protocol

IP address—a 32-bit binary number that is assigned to each computer at each packet radio station in the TCP/IP network as the identification for the routing of packets to that computer by the Internet Protocol

KA-Node—Kantronics' implementation of a node-to-node acknowledgment network protocol

KISS—an acronym for "Keep It Simple, Stupid," a Link layer non-protocol for serial input and output that supports Serial Line Interface Protocol (SLIP)

LAPB—abbreviation for Balanced Link Access Procedure

Level 2—the Link layer of OSI-RM

Level 3—the Network layer of OSI-RM

line feed—a control signal that causes a DTE display to begin printing on the next line

Link layer—Level 2 of OSI-RM that arranges data bits into frames and provides for the errorless transfer of the frames over a communications link

log off—to inform a PBBS that you are finished using the system

log on—to inform a PBBS that you wish to begin using the system

mail-forwarding—a PBBS function that allows users to send mail to users of other PBBSs

mailbox (MBO) —a packet radio and other digital modes message receiving and sending system at an individual station

mark—one of the two elements in the binary start-stop code; it often represents the on-state or 1

MBO—abbreviation for mailbox

message header—the non-data portion of a packet radio message that contains the message number, type, status, intended recipient and other routing information

meteor scatter—mode of communications that uses the ionized trails of expired meteors to reflect VHF and UHF signals

MicroSat—a series of 9-inch cube Amateur Radio satellites

minimum-shift keying (MSK)—frequency-shift keying where the shift in Hertz is equal to half the signalling rate in bits per second

Mir—the Russian space station

modem—modulator-demodulator; an electronic device that permits digital equipment to use analog communications media for data communications

modem disconnect—a connector on a TNC circuit board that facilitates the connection of an external modem and bypasses the TNC internal modem

modulate—the process of varying a carrier to represent information

moonbounce—mode of communications where VHF and UHF signals are reflected off the moon; also called Earth-to-moon-to-Earth

MSK—abbreviation for minimum-shift keying

multimode controller—TNCs that operate in other Amateur Radio modes besides packet radio *multiple connections*—the ability to establish and maintain connections with more than one station simultaneously

multiport controller—a packet radio device, such as a TNC or network node, that provides connections for more than one set of communications equipment

NET—the first TCP/IP implementation for IBM-PC/MS-DOS class computers

NET/ROM—a network and transport layer implementation for the TNC 2; it features node-to-node acknowledgment

Network layer—Level 3 of OSI-RM that routes frames through a network of links

Network Operating System (NOS)—the current TCP/IP implementation for IBM-PC/MS-DOS class computers

network—a system of interconnected packet radio stations assembled for the efficient transfer of packets over long distances

node—a junction point within a network

node-to-node acknowledgment—the networking protocol in which each node in the path of a packet informs the previous node in the path of a packet that it has received the packet correctly

non-return to zero, inverted (NRZI)—a baseband encoding technique where a data zero causes a change in signal level at the start of a bit interval, while a data one causes no change

nonvolatile RAM (NOVRAM, NVRAM, NV-RAM)—memory that stores data even while its host device is turned off

NOS—abbreviation for *Network Operating System*

NRZI—abbreviation for non-return to zero, inverted

null—a nonprinting control character that is used to insert additional time in a data string in order to compensate for slower electronic or mechanical equipment

NVRAM, NV-RAM—abbreviation for nonvolatile RAM

octet—a unit of measurement that is the equivalent of a byte or eight bits

Open Systems Interconnection Reference Model (OSI-RM)—a model formulated by the International Standards Organization that permits different computer systems to communicate with each other as long as the communication protocols used by the computer systems adhere to the model

OSI-RM—abbreviation for Open Systems Interconnection Reference Model

overhead—the non-data portion of a packet; each packet's header and trailer

Packet Internet Groper (PING)—part of the TCP/IP suite of protocols that allows one station to send a packet to another station to check if it is on the air

packet assembler/disassembler (PAD)—a device that accepts data from a DTE and formats it into packet frames for transmission via a communications medium; the PAD also accepts packet frames received via a communications medium, extracts data from the packet frame, and transfers the data to a DTE.

packet radio bulletin-board system (PBBS)—a BBS that is accessed via packet radio

PacketCluster—conferencing software designed for the exchange of DX information between stations and between nodes (clusters)

PAD—abbreviation for packet assembler/disassembler

parallel interface, parallel port—an interconnection that transfers bit-encoded information character-by-character or byte-by-byte in parallel

parity—a method of checking the accuracy of a received character by adding an extra bit in order that the character will have an even or odd number of one bits depending on the type of parity used (even or odd)

path—the route between two connected packet radio stations consisting of digipeaters, nodes and other packet stations

PBBS—abbreviation for packet radio bulletin-board system

phase-shift keying (PSK)—a method of transmitting digital information by varying the phase of a carrier between two values

PID field—abbreviation for protocol identifier field

PING—abbreviation for Packet Internet Groper

point-to-point—communications between two radio stations without assistance from an intermediary radio station

POP— abbreviation for Post Office Protocol

port—a circuit that allows a device to communicate with external devices

position—the latitude and longitude of an *APRS* station

Post Office Protocol (POP)—part of the TCP/IP suite of protocols that stores the mail for one station at another station

prioritized acknowledgment—a packet radio protocol that gives priority to packet acknowledgments

protocol—a set of recognized procedures

protocol identifier field (PID)—the field in an AX.25 frame that indicates the type of network layer protocol that is in use

PSK—abbreviation for phase-shift keying

quick brown fox message—a test message that is commonly used in RTTY, AMTOR and packet radio communications because it contains each numeral and letter of the alphabet; the complete message is THE QUICK BROWN FOX JUMPS OVER THE LAZY DOG 0123456789

The Radio Amateur Satellite Corporation (AMSAT)—an Amateur Radio organization that is responsible for United States amateur satellite developments

radio port—the TNC port that is connected to a radio transceiver (or transmitter and receiver)

RAM—abbreviation for random-access memory

random-access memory (RAM)—a data storage device that can be written to and read from

RATS Open Systems Environment (ROSE)—a networking protocol based on the virtual circuit or connection protocol; it uses node-to-node acknowledgment and network node addressing based on the CCITT X.121 numbering scheme

read-only memory (ROM)—a data storage device that can only be read

Receive Not Ready (RNR)—an AX.25 supervisory frame that indicates that the destination station is not able to accept any more information frames

Receive Ready (RR)—an AX.25 supervisory frame that indicates that the destination station is able to receive more information frames, acknowledges properly received information frames, and clears a busy condition that has been previously set by an RNR

receive state variable—a number assigned in sequence to a received packet; it is compared with the send sequence number to make sure that packets have been received in the correct order

Received Data—an EIA-232 serial interface signal that consists of data from the DCE (TNC) that was received over the communication medium and demodulated by the DCE (TNC)

REJ—abbreviation for Reject frame

Reject (REJ)—an AX.25 supervisory frame that is transmitted by the destination station to request that the source station retransmit a frame

RNR—abbreviation for Receive Not Ready frame

ROM—abbreviation for read-only memory

ROSE—abbreviation for RATS Open Systems Environment

round table—conversations between more than two stations

RR—abbreviation for Receive Ready frame

RTTY—abbreviation for radioteletype

S frame—abbreviation for Supervisory frame

SABM—abbreviation for Set Asynchronous Balanced Mode frame

SAREX—abbreviation for Shuttle Amateur Radio Experiment

secondary station identifier (SSID)—a number that follows a packet radio station call sign to differentiate between two or more packet radio stations operating under the same call sign

Send Data—an EIA-232 serial interface signal that consists of data from a DTE that is intended for transmission by the DCE (TNC) over the communication medium; also called Transmitted Data

send sequence number—a number assigned in sequence to a transmitted packet; it is compared with the receive state variable to check that packets are received in the correct order

Serial Line Interface Protocol (SLIP)—part of the TCP/IP suite of protocols that provides a simple serial data transfer between the Network layer protocols and the EIA-232 interface of the Physical layer

serial—the transfer of bit-encoded information bit-by-bit

serial interface, serial port —an interconnection that transfers bit-encoded information bit-by-bit (serially); the TNC connection for a terminal or computer

Set Asynchronous Balanced Mode (SABM)—an AX.25 unnumbered frame that initiates a connection between two packet stations

Shuttle Amateur Radio Experiments (SAREX)—the series of Amateur Radio experiments conducted aboard U.S. space shuttle missions

Signal Ground—an EIA-232 serial interface signal that provides a common ground reference for all the other interface signals except Shield (pin 1)

signaling rate—a measure of how fast individual signal elements can be transmitted through a communications system; also called symbol rate

Simple Mail Transfer Protocol (SMTP)—part of the TCP/IP suite of protocols that provides an automatic message-forwarding function

simplex—a communications mode where you transmit and receive on the same frequency

sliding window protocol—a transport layer protocol that provides end-to-end error control to counteract lost, duplicate or out-of-sequence packet frames

SLIP—abbreviation for Serial Line Interface Protocol

SMTP—abbreviation for Simple Mail Transfer Protocol

software flow control—flow control that is managed by control characters typed at the DTE or sent from the DCE (TNC)

source—the station that originates a packet frame

space—one of the two elements in the binary start-stop code; it often represents the off-state or 0

squelch tail—the transmission of an unmodulated carrier by a voice repeater after each transmission to indicate that the repeater is functioning; also called hang time

SSID—abbreviation for secondary station identifier

start bit—an extra bit that precedes a character to indicate its beginning in asynchronous communications

start character—a nonprinting control character used to restart the flow of data

station type—a specific station category in *APRS* operation

stop bit—one or two extra bits that follow a character to indicate its end in asynchronous data communications

stop character—a nonprinting control character used to stop the flow of data

store and forward—the process of receiving and holding data from one radio station for the purposes of relaying that data to another station at a later time

stream—one connection between two stations in a multiple connection application

streamswitch—a character that indicates a change in the stream being addressed in multiple connection packet radio applications

Supervisory frame (S frame)—an AX.25 frame that controls the communications link

symbol rate—a measure of how fast individual signal elements can be transmitted through a communications system; also called signalling rate

synchronous—a means of data transmission timing that uses the internal clock of a modem to synchronize data

SYSOP—abbreviation for system operator

system operator (SYSOP)—an individual who runs and maintains a bulletin-board or gateway system

T1 timer—the AX.25 timer that causes the TNC to interrogate the linked TNC when a packet is not acknowledged before the timer expires; also called the acknowledgment timer

TAPR—abbreviation for Tucson Amateur Packet Radio Corporation

TCP—abbreviation for Transmission Control Protocol

TCP/IP—abbreviation for Transmission Control Protocol/Internet Protocol; the Defense Advanced Research Projects Agency protocols that were proposed as possible network and transport layer amateur packet radio protocols by Phil Karn, KA9Q, in his amateur TCP/IP packet software

Telnet—a terminal-emulation protocol that is part of the TCP/IP suite of protocols; it provides communications with the live operator of another node

terminal—short for data terminal equipment or a computer emulating data terminal equipment

terminal emulation software—a computer program that causes a computer to function as a DTE for the purpose of transferring data over a communications medium

terminal node controller (TNC)—an Amateur Radio packet assembler/disassembler; may or may not include a modem

TexNet—a packet radio network developed by the Texas Packet Radio Society; composed of dual-port network control processors that provide AX.25 compatible user access on 2 meters and node-to-node linking at 9600 bit/s on 70 cm

TheNet—a network and transport layer implementation for the TNC 2 that is based on *NET/ROM*

throughput—the amount of data that is transferred successfully during a specific amount of time

time stamp—the process of noting the time and date of the occurrence of an event

TNC—abbreviation for terminal-node controller

TNC 1—the first TAPR TNC that was made available to the general public; it was based on the 6809 microprocessor

TNC 2—the second TAPR TNC that was made available to the general public; based on a Z80 microprocessor; its design was the most popular in amateur packet radio history

TNC emulator—computer software that performs all the functions of a TNC except the modem function

Transmission Control Protocol (TCP)—part of the TCP/IP suite of protocols that assures data integrity between the points of origination and destination

Transmitted Data—an EIA-232 serial interface signal that consists of data from a DTE that is intended for transmission by the DCE (TNC) over the communication medium; also called Send Data

transparent mode—the TNC mode that permits the transfer of data that is "invisible" to the TNC; it is used when it is necessary to transfer control characters that may be imbedded in data

Tucson Amateur Packet Radio Corporation (TAPR)—the Arizona-based Amateur Radio organization that was instrumental in packet radio protocol and hardware developments in the United States

turnaround time—the time required to switch between the receive and transmit modes in a half-duplex application

type-in flow control—flow control that causes the TNC to stop sending characters to the DTE whenever a character is entered at the DTE keyboard; prevents displayed received characters from interfering with the display of keyed characters

U frame—abbreviation for unnumbered frame

UA—abbreviation for Unnumbered Acknowledge frame

UDP—abbreviation for User Datagram Protocol

UI—abbreviation for Unnumbered Information frame

unconnected packets—packets transmitted from a source station with no specific destination station being addressed; used for beacons, CQs, and round table communications

Unnumbered Acknowledge (UA)—an AX.25 unnumbered frame that acknowledges receipt and acceptance of an SABM or DISC frame

Unnumbered frame (U frame)—an AX.25 frame that controls the communications link and provides the capability to transmit frames containing information without a specified destination

Unnumbered Information (UI)—an AX.25 unnumbered frame that allows data to be transmitted from a source station with no specific destination station being addressed

upload—to send files to a PBBS or other packet radio station

User Datagram Protocol (UDP)—part of the TCP/IP suite of protocols that performs miscellaneous functions

user interface—the set of TNC commands and status messages that are available to the user

VADCG—abbreviation for Vancouver Amateur Digital Communications Group

Vancouver Amateur Digital Communications Group (VADCG)—a Canada-based Amateur Radio organization that was responsible for the first popular packet radio protocol and hardware developments in Amateur Radio

VDT—abbreviation for video-display terminal

video-display terminal (VDT)—an input and output device that uses a cathode ray tube for output

virtual circuit—the appearance of a direct connection between the source and destination of a packet

virtual circuit protocol —a Network layer protocol that sets up and maintains a clearly defined path for the transfer of packets between a source and destination during a single data communications session; also called connection protocol

WØRLI MailBox—public domain PBBS software written by Hank Oredson, WØRLI

wormhole—the part of a packet radio link that uses a non-Amateur Radio medium, such as an orbiting satellite or a telephone line

X.25—a packet switching protocol formulated by the CCITT

Xoff—transmitter off; a flow control character used in ASCII file transfers; it commands the transmitter to stop sending data.

Xon—transmitter on; a flow control character used in ASCII file transfers; it commands the transmitter to continue sending data.

zero bit insertion—a process that prevents the other AX.25 fields from having the same unique contents of the flag field; also called bit stuffing

G

ASCII Character Set

The following table lists the ASCII character set including the decimal, hexadecimal, and binary value of each character and the name of each control character.

Character	*Decimal*	*Hex*	*Binary*	*Name*
NUL	0	00	00000000	null
CTRL-A (SOH)	1	01	00000001	start of heading
CTRL-B (STX)	2	02	00000010	start of text
CTRL-C (ETX)	3	03	00000011	end of text
CTRL-D (EOT)	4	04	00000100	end of transmission
CTRL-E (ENQ)	5	05	00000101	enquiry
CTRL-F (ACK)	6	06	00000110	acknowledge
CTRL-G (BEL)	7	07	00000111	bell
CTRL-H (BS)	8	08	00001000	backspace
CTRL-I (HT)	9	09	00001001	horizontal tab
CTRL-J (LF)	10	0A	00001010	line feed
CTRL-K (VT)	11	0B	00001011	vertical tab
CTRL-L (FF)	12	0C	00001100	form feed
CTRL-M (CR)	13	0D	00001101	carriage return
CTRL-N (SO)	14	0E	00001110	shift out
CTRL-O (SI)	15	0F	00001111	shift in
CTRL-P (DLE)	16	10	00010000	data link escape
CTRL-Q (DC1/XON)	17	11	00010001	device control 1/X on
CTRL-R (DC2)	18	12	00010010	device control 2

Character	*Decimal*	*Hex*	*Binary*	*Name*
CTRL-S (DC3/XOFF)	19	13	00010011	device control 3/X off
CTRL-T (DC4)	20	14	00010100	device control 4
CTRL-U (NAK)	21	15	00010101	negative acknowledge
CTRL-V (SYN)	22	16	00010110	synchronous idle
CTRL-W (ETB)	23	17	00010111	end of block
CTRL-X (CAN)	24	18	00011000	cancel
CTRL-Y (EM)	25	19	00011001	end of medium
CTRL-Z (SUB)	26	1A	00011010	substitute
ESC	27	1B	00011011	escape
FS	28	1C	00011100	file separator
GS	29	1D	00011101	group separator
RS	30	1E	00011110	record separator
US	31	1F	00011111	unit separator
SP	32	20	00100000	space
!	33	21	00100001	
"	34	22	00100010	
#	35	23	00100011	
$	36	24	00100100	
%	37	25	00100101	
&	38	26	00100110	
'	39	27	00100111	apostrophe
(	40	28	00101000	
)	41	29	00101001	
*	42	2A	00101010	
+	43	2B	00101011	
,	44	2C	00101100	comma
-	45	2D	00101101	
.	46	2E	00101110	
/	47	2F	00101111	
0	48	30	00110000	
1	49	31	00110001	
2	50	32	00110010	
3	51	33	00110011	
4	52	34	00110100	
5	53	35	00110101	
6	54	36	00110110	
7	55	37	00110111	
8	56	38	00111000	
9	57	39	00111001	
:	58	3A	00111010	
;	59	3B	00111011	
<	60	3C	00111100	
=	61	3D	00111101	
>	62	3E	00111110	
?	63	3F	00111111	
@	64	40	01000000	
A	65	41	01000001	
B	66	42	01000010	
C	67	43	01000011	
D	68	44	01000100	
E	69	45	01000101	

Character	*Decimal*	*Hex*	*Binary*	*Name*
F	70	46	01000110	
G	71	47	01000111	
H	72	48	01001000	
I	73	49	01001001	
J	74	4A	01001010	
K	75	4B	01001011	
L	76	4C	01001100	
M	77	4D	01001101	
N	78	4E	01001110	
O	79	4F	01001111	
P	80	50	01010000	
Q	81	51	01010001	
R	82	52	01010010	
S	83	53	01010011	
T	84	54	01010100	
U	85	55	01010101	
V	86	56	01010110	
W	87	57	01010111	
X	88	58	01011000	
Y	89	59	01011001	
Z	90	5A	01011010	
[	91	5B	01011011	
\	92	5C	01011100	
]	93	5D	01011101	
^	94	5E	01011110	
_	95	5F	01011111	
`	96	60	01100000	
a	97	61	01100001	
b	98	62	01100010	
c	99	63	01100011	
d	100	64	01100100	
e	101	65	01100101	
f	102	66	01100110	
g	103	67	01100111	
h	104	68	01101000	
i	105	69	01101001	
j	106	6A	01101010	
k	107	6B	01101011	
l	108	6C	01101100	
m	109	6D	01101101	
n	110	6E	01101110	
o	111	6F	01101111	
p	112	70	01110000	
q	113	71	01110001	
r	114	72	01110010	
s	115	73	01110011	
t	116	74	01110100	
u	117	75	01110101	
v	118	76	01110110	
w	119	77	01110111	
x	120	78	01111000	

Character	*Decimal*	*Hex*	*Binary*	*Name*
y	121	79	01111001	
z	122	7A	01111010	
{	123	7B	01111011	
|	124	7C	01111100	
}	125	7D	01111101	
~	126	7E	01111110	
DEL	127	7F	01111111	delete
	128	80	10000000	
	129	81	10000001	
	130	82	10000010	
	131	83	10000011	
	132	84	10000100	
	133	85	10000101	
	134	86	10000110	
	135	87	10000111	
	136	88	10001000	
	137	89	10001001	
	138	8A	10001010	
	139	8B	10001011	
	140	8C	10001100	
	141	8D	10001101	
	142	8E	10001110	
	143	8F	10001111	
	144	90	10010000	
	145	91	10010001	
	146	92	10010010	
	147	93	10010011	
	148	94	10010100	
	149	95	10010101	
	150	96	10010110	
	151	97	10010111	
	152	98	10011000	
	153	99	10011001	
	154	9A	10011010	
	155	9B	10011011	
	156	9C	10011100	
	157	9D	10011101	
	158	9E	10011110	
	159	9F	10011111	
	160	A0	10100000	
	161	A1	10100001	
	162	A2	10100010	
	163	A3	10100011	
	164	A4	10100100	
	165	A5	10100101	
	166	A6	10100110	
	167	A7	10100111	
	168	A8	10101000	
	169	A9	10101001	
	170	AA	10101010	
	171	AB	10101011	

Character	Decimal	Hex	Binary	Name
	172	AC	10101100	
	173	AD	10101101	
	174	AE	10101110	
	175	AF	10101111	
	176	B0	10110000	
	177	B1	10110001	
	178	B2	10110010	
	179	B3	10110011	
	180	B4	10110100	
	181	B5	10110101	
	182	B6	10110110	
	183	B7	10110111	
	184	B8	10111000	
	185	B9	10111001	
	186	BA	10111010	
	187	BB	10111011	
	188	BC	10111100	
	189	BD	10111101	
	190	BE	10111110	
	191	BF	10111111	
	192	C0	11000000	
	193	C1	11000001	
	194	C2	11000010	
	195	C3	11000011	
	196	C4	11000100	
	197	C5	11000101	
	198	C6	11000110	
	199	C7	11000111	
	200	C8	11001000	
	201	C9	11001001	
	202	CA	11001010	
	203	CB	11001011	
	204	CC	11001100	
	205	CD	11001101	
	206	CE	11001110	
	207	CF	11001111	
	208	D0	11010000	
	209	D1	11010001	
	210	D2	11010010	
	211	D3	11010011	
	212	D4	11010100	
	213	D5	11010101	
	214	D6	11010110	
	215	D7	11010111	
	216	D8	11011000	
	217	D9	11011001	
	218	DA	11011010	
	219	DB	11011011	
	220	DC	11011100	
	221	DD	11011101	
	222	DE	11011110	

Character	Decimal	Hex	Binary	Name
	223	DF	11011111	
	224	E0	11100000	
	225	E1	11100001	
	226	E2	11100010	
	227	E3	11100011	
	228	E4	11100100	
	229	E5	11100101	
	230	E6	11100110	
	231	E7	11100111	
	232	E8	11101000	
	233	E9	11101001	
	234	EA	11101010	
	235	EB	11101011	
	236	EC	11101100	
	237	ED	11101101	
	238	EE	11101110	
	239	EF	11101111	
	240	F0	11110000	
	241	F1	11110001	
	242	F2	11110010	
	243	F3	11110011	
	244	F4	11110100	
	245	F5	11110101	
	246	F6	11110110	
	247	F7	11110111	
	248	F8	11111000	
	249	F9	11111001	
	250	FA	11111010	
	251	FB	11111011	
	252	FC	11111100	
	253	FD	11111101	
	254	FE	11111110	
	255	FF	11111111	

The Author

Stan Horzepa, WA1LOU, first licensed in 1969, is an Amateur Extra Class licensee and an ARRL life member. As former Communications Assistant of the Public Service branch of the ARRL's old Communications Department, Stan edited two editions of the *Repeater Directory* and started *QST*'s "FM/RPT" column. After leaving ARRL headquarters, Stan started *QST*'s "On Line" column and became editor of *Gateway: The ARRL Packet-Radio Newsletter*. Stan also wrote the ARRL's first packet radio book, *Your Packet Gateway to Packet Radio,* and currently writes *QST*'s "Packet Perspective" column, which he started in March 1990.

Stan has also contributed to editions of *The ARRL Operating Manual*, *The ARRL Handbook for the Radio Amateur* and *Operating an Amateur Radio Station*. Besides his Amateur Radio writing achievements, Stan has held a number of ARRL appointments (ASCM, NM, OBS, ORS, OVS) and is the former Section Communications Manager of Connecticut. He also has numerous operating awards including A-1 Operator, BPL, DXCC, Public Service, PSHR, WAC, WAS, The Polska Award, and a Central Radio Club Cosmos silver medal.

WA1LOU lives with his wife Laurie and daughter Hayley in Wolcott, Connecticut on top of Compounce Mountain. He has a BA from the University of Connecticut, a JD from Western New England College, and is supervisor of technical writing for General DataComm, Inc. Needless to say, Stan is active on packet radio (mostly 2 meters). Packet-radio mail can be sent to WA1LOU@N4GAA.CT.USA.NOAM and electronic mail can be sent to 70645.247@compuserve.com and horzepa@gdc.com.

About The American Radio Relay League

The seed for Amateur Radio was planted in the 1890s, when Guglielmo Marconi began his experiments in wireless telegraphy. Soon he was joined by dozens, then hundreds, of others who were enthusiastic about sending and receiving messages through the air—some with a commercial interest, but others solely out of a love for this new communications medium. The United States government began licensing Amateur Radio operators in 1912.

By 1914, there were thousands of Amateur Radio operators—hams—in the United States. Hiram Percy Maxim, a leading Hartford, Connecticut, inventor and industrialist saw the need for an organization to band together this fledgling group of radio experimenters. In May 1914 he founded the American Radio Relay League (ARRL) to meet that need.

Today ARRL, with more than 170,000 members, is the largest organization of radio amateurs in the United States. The League is a not-for-profit organization that:

- promotes interest in Amateur Radio communications and experimentation
- represents US radio amateurs in legislative matters, and
- maintains fraternalism and a high standard of conduct among Amateur Radio operators.

At League headquarters in the Hartford suburb of Newington, the staff helps serve the needs of members. ARRL is also International Secretariat for the International Amateur Radio Union, which is made up of similar societies in more than 100 countries around the world.

ARRL publishes the monthly journal *QST*, as well as newsletters and many publications covering all aspects of Amateur Radio. Its headquarters station, W1AW, transmits bulletins of interest to radio amateurs and Morse code practice sessions. The League also coordinates an extensive field organization, which includes volunteers who provide technical information for radio amateurs and public-service activities. ARRL also represents US amateurs with the Federal Communications Commission and other government agencies in the US and abroad.

Membership in ARRL means much more than receiving *QST* each month. In addition to the services already described, ARRL offers membership services on a personal level, such as the ARRL Volunteer Examiner Coordinator Program and a QSL bureau.

Full ARRL membership (available only to licensed radio amateurs) gives you a voice in how the affairs of the organization are governed. League policy is set by a Board of Directors (one from each of 15 Divisions). Each year, half of the ARRL Board of Directors stands for election by the full members they represent. The day-to-day operation of ARRL HQ is managed by an Executive Vice President and a Chief Financial Officer.

No matter what aspect of Amateur Radio attracts you, ARRL membership is relevant and important. There would be no Amateur Radio as we know it today were it not for the ARRL. We would be happy to welcome you as a member! (An Amateur Radio license is not required for Associate Membership.) For more information about ARRL and answers to any questions you may have about Amateur Radio, write or call:

ARRL Educational Activities Dept
225 Main Street
Newington CT 06111-1494
(860) 594-0200
Prospective new amateurs call:
800-32-NEW HAM (800-326-3942)

W1AW schedule

Pacific	Mtn	Cent	East	Sun	Mon	Tue	Wed	Thu	Fri	Sat
6 am	7 am	8 am	9 am			Fast Code	Slow Code	Fast Code	Slow Code	
7 am	8 am	9 am	10 am			Code Bulletin				
8 am	9 am	10 am	11 am			Teleprinter Bulletin				
9 am	10 am	11 am	noon							
10 am	11 am	noon	1 pm		Visiting Operator Time					
11 am	noon	1 pm	2 pm							
noon	1 pm	2 pm	3 pm							
1 pm	2 pm	3 pm	4 pm	Slow Code	Fast Code	Slow Code	Fast Code	Slow Code	Fast Code	Slow Code
2 pm	3 pm	4 pm	5 pm	Code Bulletin						
3 pm	4 pm	5 pm	6 pm	Teleprinter Bulletin						
4 pm	5 pm	6 pm	7 pm	Fast Code	Slow Code	Fast Code	Slow Code	Fast Code	Slow Code	Fast Code
5 pm	6 pm	7 pm	8 pm	Code Bulletin						
6 pm	7 pm	8 pm	9 pm	Teleprinter Bulletin						
6^{45} pm	7^{45} pm	8^{45} pm	9^{45} pm	Voice Bulletin						
7 pm	8 pm	9 pm	10 pm	Slow Code	Fast Code	Slow Code	Fast Code	Slow Code	Fast Code	Slow Code
8 pm	9 pm	10 pm	11 pm	Code Bulletin						
9 pm	10 pm	11 pm	Mdnte	Teleprinter Bulletin						
9^{45} pm	10^{45} pm	11^{45} pm	12^{45} am	Voice Bulletin						

W1AW's schedule is at the same local time throughout the year. The schedule according to your local time will change if your local time does not have seasonal adjustments that are made at the same time as North American time changes between standard time and daylight time. From the first Sunday in April to the last Sunday in October, UTC = Eastern Time + 4 hours. For the rest of the year, UTC = Eastern Time + 5 hours.

❑ ***Morse code transmissions:***

Frequencies are 1.818, 3.5815, 7.0475, 14.0475, 18.0975, 21.0675, 28.0675 and 147.555 MHz.

Slow Code = practice sent at 5, 7½, 10, 13 and 15 wpm.

Fast Code = practice sent at 35, 30, 25, 20, 15, 13 and 10 wpm.

Code practice text is from the pages of *QST*. The source is given at the beginning of each practice session and alternate speeds within each session. For example, "Text is from July 1992 *QST*, pages 9 and 81," indicates that the plain text is from the article on page 9 and mixed number/letter groups are from page 81.

Code bulletins are sent at 18 wpm.

W1AW qualifying runs are sent on the same frequencies as the Morse code transmissions. West Coast qualifying runs are transmitted on approximately 3.590 MHz by W6OWP, with W6ZRJ and AB6YR as alternates. At the beginning of each code practice session, the schedule for the next qualifying run is presented. Underline one minute of the highest speed you copied, certify that your copy was made without aid, and send it to ARRL for grading. Please include your name, call sign (if any) and complete mailing address. Send a 9×12-inch SASE for a certificate, or a business-size SASE for an endorsement.

❑ ***Teleprinter transmissions:***

Frequencies are 3.625, 7.095, 14.095, 18.1025, 21.095, 28.095 and 147.555 MHz.

Bulletins are sent at 45.45-baud Baudot and 100-baud AMTOR, FEC Mode B. 110-baud ASCII will be sent only as time allows.

On Tuesdays and Saturdays at 6:30 PM Eastern Time, Keplerian elements for many amateur satellites are sent on the regular teleprinter frequencies.

❑ ***Voice transmissions:***

Frequencies are 1.855, 3.99, 7.29, 14.29, 18.16, 21.39, 28.59 and 147.555 MHz.

❑ ***Miscellanea:***

On Fridays, UTC, a DX bulletin replaces the regular bulletins.

W1AW is open to visitors during normal operating hours: from 1 PM until 1 AM on Mondays, 9 AM until 1 AM Tuesday through Friday, from 1 PM to 1 AM on Saturdays, and from 3:30 PM to 1 AM on Sundays. FCC licensed amateurs may operate the station from 1 to 4 PM Monday through Saturday. Be sure to bring your current FCC amateur license or a photocopy.

In a communication emergency, monitor W1AW for special bulletins as follows: voice on the hour, teleprinter at 15 minutes past the hour, and CW on the half hour.

Headquarters and W1AW are closed on New Year's Day, President's Day, Good Friday, Memorial Day, Independence Day, Labor Day, Thanksgiving and the following Friday, and Christmas Day. On the first Thursday of September, Headquarters and W1AW will be closed during the afternoon.

Index

A

B

C

D

E-F

G

H

I-L

R

S

T

U-Z

We're At Your Service

ARRL Headquarters is open from 8 AM to 5 PM Eastern Time, Monday through Friday, except holidays. Our address is: 225 Main St, Newington, CT 06111-1494. You can call us at 860-594-0200, or fax us at 860-594-0259.

If you have a question, try one of these Headquarters departments . . .

	Contact	*Telephone*	*Electronic Mail*
Joining ARRL	Membership Desk	888-277-5289	**circulation@arrl.org**
***QST* Delivery**	Circulation Desk	860-594-0338	**circulation@arrl.org**
Publication Orders	Sales Desk	888-277-5289	**pubsales@arrl.org**
M-F Only, 8 AM to 8 PM Eastern Time		**(toll free)**	
Regulatory Info		860-594-0323	**reginfo@arrl.org**
Exams	VEC	860-594-0300	**vec@arrl.org**
Educational Materials	Educational Activities	860-594-0301	**ead@arrl.org**
Contests		860-594-0252	**contest@arrl.org**
Technical Questions	ARRL Lab	860-594-0214	**tis@arrl.org**
Awards		860-594-0288	**awards@arrl.org**
DXCC/VUCC		860-594-0234	**dxcc@arrl.org**
Advertising		860-594-0207	**ads@arrl.org**
Media Relations		860-594-0328	**newsmedia@arrl.org**
QSL Service		860-594-0274	**buro@arrl.org**
Scholarships		860-594-0230	**foundation@arrl.org**
Emergency Comm		860-594-0261	**k1ce@arrl.org**
Clubs		860-594-0264	**clubs@arrl.org**
Hamfests		860-594-0262	**hamfests@arrl.org**

You can send e-mail to any ARRL Headquarters employee if you know his or her name or call sign. The second half of every Headquarters e-mail address is **@arrl.org**. To create the first half, simply use the person's call sign. If you don't know their call sign, use the first letter of their first name, followed by their complete last name. For example, to send a message to John Hennessee, N1KB, Regulatory Information Specialist, you could address it to **jhennessee@arrl.org** or **N1KB@arrl.org**.

If all else fails, send e-mail to **hq@arrl.org** and it will be routed to the right people or departments.

ARRL on the On-Line Services

We maintain accounts on these major on-line services and check for mail several times daily.

Service	*ARRL Address*
CompuServe	70007,3373
America Online	HQARRL1

ARRL BBS

The ARRL *Hiram* Bulletin Board System is as close as your telephone. Hiram offers more than a thousand software files for your enjoyment. You can also use Hiram to send messages to anyone at Headquarters—or to other hams who frequent the BBS. Hiram accepts up to four simultaneous connections at rates from 1200 to 28,800 baud. Fire up your modem and call 860-594-0306.

Technical Information Server

If you have Internet e-mail capability, you can tap into the ARRL Technical Information Server, otherwise known as the *Info Server*. To have user instructions and a handy index sent to you automatically, simply address an e-mail message to: **info@arrl.org** Subject: **Info Request** In the body of your message enter:

HELP
SEND INDEX
QUIT

ARRL on the World Wide Web

You'll also find the ARRL on the World Wide Web at:

http://www.arrl.org/

At the ARRL Web page you'll find the latest W1AW bulletins, a hamfest calendar, exam schedules, an on-line ARRL Publications Catalog and much more. We're always adding new features to our Web page, so check it often!

Stopping by for a visit?

We offer tours of Headquarters and W1AW at 9, 10 and 11 AM, and at 1, 2 and 3 PM, Monday to Friday (except holidays). Special tour times may be arranged in advance. Bring your license and you can operate W1AW anytime between 1 and 4 PM!

ARRL Headquarters is within easy driving distance from Interstates 84 or 91. In addition, Hartford is served by Amtrak, with several trains daily from New York, Boston and beyond (call 1-800-USA-RAIL for more information). Bradley International Airport in Windsor Locks, Connecticut (about 20 miles north of Headquarters), is served by many major carriers.

Would you like to write for QST?

We're always looking for new material of interest to hams. Send a self-addressed, stamped envelope (postage for 2 oz) and ask for a copy of the *Author's Guide*. (It's also available via the ARRL Info Server, and via the World Wide Web at **http://www.arrl.org/qst/aguide/**.) The guide contains all the information you'll need to craft an article to meet our requirements. Send article ideas or manuscripts to the attention of the *QST* Editor (e-mail **qst@arrl.org**).

Press Releases and New Products/Books

Send your press releases and new book announcements to the attention of the ***QST* Editor** (e-mail **qst@arrl.org**). New product announcements should be sent to the Product Review Editor (e-mail **reviews@arrl.org**).

Strays and Up Front

Send your Strays and Up Front materials to the *QST* Features Editor (e-mail **upfront@arrl.org**). Be sure to include your name, address and daytime telephone number.

Interested in Becoming a Ham?

Just pick up the telephone and call toll free 1-800-326-3942, or send e-mail to **newham@arrl.org**. We'll provide helpful advice on obtaining your Amateur Radio license, and we'll be happy to send you our informative Prospective Ham Package.

ARRL Audio News

The best way to keep up with fast-moving events in the ham community is to listen to the ARRL Audio News. It's as close as your telephone at 860-594-0384, or on the Web at **http://www.arrl.org/arrlletter/audio/**.

PRACTICAL PACKET RADIO

PROOF OF PURCHASE

FEEDBACK

Please use this form to give us your comments on this book and what you'd like to see in future editions. You can also e-mail your comments to us at **pubsfdbk@arrl.org** (publications feedback). In that case, please be sure to include your name, call, e-mail address and the book title and edition in the body of your e-mail message. Also indicate whether or not you are an ARRL member.

Where did you purchase this book?
☐ From ARRL directly ☐ From an ARRL dealer

Is there a dealer who carries ARRL publications within:
☐ 5 miles ☐ 15 miles ☐ 30 miles of your location? ☐ Not sure.

License class:

☐ Novice	☐ Technician	☐ Technician Plus
☐ General	☐ Advanced	☐ Extra

Name ______________________________

Call Sign ______________________ ARRL member? ☐ Yes ☐ No

Daytime Phone ( ) ______________ Age ______________

Address ______________________________

City, State/Province, ZIP/Postal Code ______________________

If licensed, how long? ______________

Other hobbies ______________

Occupation ______________

For ARRL use only	PPR
Edition	1 2 3 4 5 6 7 8 9 10 11 12
Printing	2 3 4 5 6 7 8 9 10 11 12

From ______________________

____

____

Please affix postage. Post Office will not deliver without postage.

EDITOR, PRACTICAL PACKET RADIO
AMERICAN RADIO RELAY LEAGUE
225 MAIN ST
NEWINGTON CT 06111-1494

.... please fold and tape ....